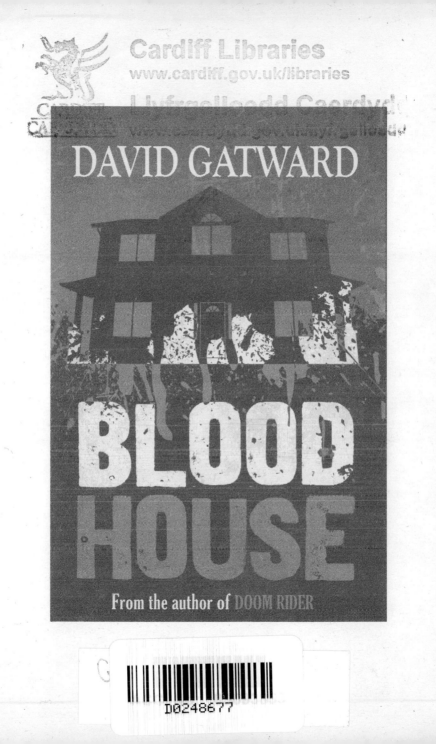

DAVID GATWARD

BLOOD HOUSE

From the author of DOOM RIDER

Also by David Gatward

The Dead

The Dark

The Damned

Doom Rider

The Cave

To The Extreme

Booksurfers

DAVID GATWARD

BLOOD HOUSE

EDGE
FRANKLIN WATTS

LONDON·SYDNEY

Part of the **RIVETS** series

This edition published in 2012
by Franklin Watts

Text © David Gatward 2012
Cover design by Peter Scoulding

Franklin Watts
338 Euston Road
London NW1 3BH

Franklin Watts Australia
Level 17/207 Kent Street
Sydney, NSW 2000

Pavel Khorenyan/istockphoto: front cover b.
Laschi/Shutterstock: front cover t.

ISBN: 978 1 4451 1468 2

1 3 5 7 9 10 8 6 4 2

Printed in Great Britain

Franklin Watts is a division of Hachette Children's Books,
an Hachette UK company.
www.hachette.co.uk

To Black Inc: the blood was worth it.

"The monster was the best friend I ever had."

Boris Karloff

"That truth is that monsters are real,
and ghosts are real, too. They live inside us,
and sometimes they win."

Stephen King

CONTENTS

CHAPTER ONE

Trev couldn't remember exactly
when he'd been brought to the
country house hospital. But he
could remember the sounds:
a gate locking behind him,
footsteps echoing in a corridor,

clinical voices.

His room was white: white door, white walls, white bed and a small, white frosted-glass window which burned with the bright white light of the daytime.

Trev could only see red.

Blood red.
Torn flesh.
Red blood.

He still couldn't wash the stain from his hands.
It can't be real, can't be real, can't be real, can't be real...

The door opened like a yawning mouth and a doctor walked in. Two other men, who looked like twin gorillas, followed him. They stared at Trev as though they wanted him to burst into flames.

"How are we today?"

Trev didn't respond. He was staring at the walls, the window, the pipe work. Looking for clues, looking for teeth.

The doctor, his dark hair a hole torn in the whiteness above his head, was holding a clipboard and chewing a pencil. His white lab coat made him almost invisible against the walls.

Almost wasn't good enough, thought Trev. Because the beast knew where you were, would always find you.

"Sleep well?"

Trev shrugged, rubbed his hands together.

"The blackouts? The nightmares?"

"Not nightmares," Trev whispered. "Memories."

The doctor wrote something on his clipboard. One of the gorillas walked over carrying a folding chair. The doctor sat down.

"Ready to talk about what happened?"

Trev shook his head. Talking was pointless. No one listened. No one believed.

"What about this?"

The doctor held something out.

It was a motorcycle helmet that looked like it had barely survived a road accident.

Trev stared at his reflection in the mirrored visor. His eyes were black pools, empty, cold. Hunter's eyes.

"You were wearing it when they found you," said the doctor. "What about this?"

Trev had seen the photograph a thousand times: a normal hallway in a normal detached house in a normal part of the city. Except that this hallway looked like an abattoir. Something alive had been torn apart in that place, ripped limb from limb. Hadn't stood a chance.

"What happened to your family in this house, Trevor?"

Don't make me remember...

"Who did this?"

Not who, what...

"Was it you?"

Trev was off the bed in a beat. Like a tiger dragging its kill to the

ground, he slammed the doctor
onto the floor, winding him,
knocking the helmet to skitter
across the floor.

"They were my parents! My
kid sister!" Trev spat, loud and
desperate.

The gorillas yanked Trev away
to restrain him.

"It was the bloody house!" he
screamed, his skin burning against
the rough hands holding him.
"It took them! Why won't you
believe me?"

Trev was crying now, with the pain of being held, the pain of the memory, the pain of knowing no one would ever believe him that the house had come alive. That it hadn't been a house at all, just something waiting for the right moment to spring the trap. A beast hungry for blood.

The pinprick in the side of his neck came as no surprise.

The room melted to darkness.

CHAPTER TWO

Trev woke screaming. He was
breathing hard, the images of
those last moments in that house
burning in his mind like a witch
at the stake. The house coming
to life. The howls of his parents

as they'd been hacked apart. The
gurgling yells from his sister. And
the heat of raw anger from the
very walls as Trev had smashed his
way out into the back garden.

Alive.

Trev saw that his door was bent
and buckled and open. A silence
hung in the air like fog. He sat up
to lean back against the wall, the
cold plaster stinging his skin.

"Hello?"

Trev went to the door. It was
marked and smeared with blood.

As he tried to close it, the hinges
squealed and the metallic echo
rattled away from him like a
steel ball down a drainpipe. Trev
backed away towards his bed,
crawled across it, the duvet
racking up behind him.

Scared now, he rubbed his
face and saw red on his hand, his
whole arm. It was everywhere.
Just like before, at the first
house. And not just on him, but
on his bed, running down the
white walls like spilled paint.

The window of his room

exploded with the crack of a gunshot, scattering glass like hail. The room went dark. It had never been daylight at all, just a bulb.

A distant scream ripped the air. Then another sound shook the building, like rocks tumbling into the back of a dump truck. Trev went to lean back against the wall but a gap swallowed him and he crashed onto the floor, cracking his head.

Scrambling to his feet, Trev glared at the wall, at the bed, at the gap now between them of about two feet that hadn't even existed a moment ago.

Oh god, it's here...

Trev shuddered as though an arctic wind had just blasted into the room. There would be no calming down. Not now. Not ever.

A movement in the corridor hooked Trev's eyes round like a fish caught on a well-cast fly. For a moment, there was nothing. Then a light flickered and he saw a figure stumbling desperately towards him, bouncing into the walls, falling and tumbling.

It was the doctor, his white coat ripped and torn and spattered with blood. His face was shredded, one of his eyes gone, the other staring wildly through a purple-black bruise. His left foot was twisted horribly, and he was running along with it flapping from one side to the other, the bones crunching with each and every step.

The doctor slammed into Trev's room and slid across the floor on his belly. The bits of shattered, smashed glass cut into him like

tiny razors. Then he crawled into
a corner, whimpering.

Trev stared at the doctor, made
no sound. The beast had done
this, but the doctor had somehow
survived. His eyes ever flitting to
the corridor, Trev pulled the duvet
off the bed and lay it on the
ground to crawl safely across the
floor. The doctor jumped at the
sound, tried to push himself into
the wall. As Trev reached out to
reassure him, a scream ripped out
of the man's mouth of smashed
teeth and blood,and he arched his

back, and grabbed Trev round the
throat.

CHAPTER THREE

Trev yanked the doctor's hands from round his neck, slapped him away.

"I told you," he said. "But you wouldn't believe me, would you?"

Hearing Trev's voice, the doctor

shrunk away and frantically started to search through his own pockets. He pulled out a mobile phone, but it slipped from his hands.

The doctor shook his head, pointed a quivering finger at Trev. "Beast... monster..."

"It preys on humans," said Trev. The doctor was shaking, weeping, scraping at the walls as though to escape. "It hides itself where we'd never think to look; our homes, our buildings, a hospital."

Trev knew the beast in the

brickwork was coming for him. Adrenalin blasted through his veins like napalm. He'd escaped once before, he would do it again.

Outside his room, the corridor was free of smashed glass and, as Trev made to stand, he saw something under the bed, shoved up against the back wall. It was the motorcycle helmet, no doubt left behind after the scuffle with the doctor earlier. He pulled it out, stared at his reflection again, and in it saw the walls behind him split, saw teeth. He heard the doctor move and watched him stumble into a terrified sprint to race out of the room.

Trev dashed into the corridor, the helmet in his hand. The doctor was gone. Across from him, something caught his eye. A fire axe leaning against the wall beneath the smashed box that had once contained it, its shaft and head badly bloodied. Trev grabbed the axe, gave no thought as to why it was loose. It felt good to have some protection at least.

He ran on. Doors flickered past. Some were closed, others smashed in. Trev did his best to stare straight ahead, but it was impossible to ignore the scarlet tableaus the beast had created from the hospital's residents.

Barely holding onto what little sanity he had left, Trev slammed into a wall as the corridor ended in a T-junction. His eyes darted left, then right, then left again. Lights flickered. The building groaned like something, somewhere was being swallowed.

Along the left corridor, Trev spotted a flight of stairs rising upwards. Remembering the bulb outside the window in his room, he knew then that he was underground. And going up was his only way out.

Trev forced his muscles to ignore his fear and to move. He was at the stairs in seconds, bounding up them three at a time, rounded a landing, raced up another flight.

Another corridor. More doors. Which way?

"Trevor!"

The voice cut through Trev like a sabre.

"Trevor! This way! Quickly!"

He didn't want to look, because that voice was long gone now, a memory. But that little bit of him that wanted it to be real, despite everything that had happened, forced his head to turn, to glance over his left shoulder and down the corridor.

It was a girl. No older than eight. It was his kid sister.

CHAPTER FOUR

"Katie..."

"This way," said the little girl, beckoning to him. "Come on!"

"You're dead," Trev replied, his voice cracking like he couldn't quite tune himself in. "The house took you. I heard you scream!"

The girl waved more frantically. "You have to believe me! Come on! Quickly!"

Trev took a step forwards, the axe heavy in his hands, ready to swing.

"I survived!" said the girl. "The beast doesn't know, but I did!"

Trev was walking now. This was Katie, his sister! She would never lie to him, would she? It had to be her! She was flesh and bone and he could see her deep brown eyes, the freckles on her face.

"In here!" the girl said. "Your mum and dad are here, too! Come on!"

Trev jarred to a halt, the helmet dropped from his hand.

"What?"

The girl's smile flickered. "In here!"

"No, what you said after that," said Trev.

"Mum and Dad," said the girl. "They're in here. Quickly!"

Trev moved no closer. The image of the girl shimmered like a heat wave.

"That's not what you said," he muttered. "Your mum and dad? Katie would never have said it like that. They were our parents. Not mine. You got it wrong. Who or whatever you are, you got it so wrong."

The girl's face broke into a snarl. "You're wasting time!"

Trev picked up the helmet, put it on. And the world changed.

Where walls had been, he saw veins, flesh and slime. The corridor was a tube, and things were coming for him, awful eyeless things with tentacles and teeth.

The girl yelled out, but through the helmet's visor Trev saw the truth as the girl's mouth pulled open with such force her jaw snapped off. She screamed then, and out came thick, black tentacles where her tongue should have been. They flicked at the air as though tasting it, then blasted towards Trev.

Trev stumbled as a tentacle sliced into his skin with the ease of a scalpel. Another came for his head, but the helmet saved him. He swung the axe, then ran as behind him the thing that had been his sister broke apart and was swallowed by the walls.

Too late Trev saw the dark pool ahead. It caught him off guard and sent him sliding down the corridor to slam into the inside,

mirrored walls of a lift, smashing
them to pieces. The lift doors
closed behind him.

Darkness.

CHAPTER FIVE

The doors opened. Bright light
stabbed Trev's eyes. He was not in
a basement of brick and concrete,
but in a tube the colour of dark
blood, held up by vast bones, like
ribs.

Trev wiped the axe clean, gripped it tight and walked forwards. Anger seethed in him. The beast had taken his family, used his sister as bait, killed again and again, then finally lured him deep into its belly.

"You want me, then you come get me!" he screamed and heaved the axe into the wall of the tube. The stabbed section of the wall split like a balloon and pink gore flooded out.

"Come on!" Trev yelled again. "What are you waiting for? Not hungry now, is that it?"

The floor bucked and Trev toppled forwards into the pink muck. Then the tunnel started to tip upwards and Trev started to slide. He grabbed the axe, jammed it into the floor. For a moment it held, but as the tunnel grew ever steeper, the axe started to move. Then gravity got its way, and Trev slid downwards, opening the tunnel up behind him like a box cutter down the side of a tent.

Trev slammed into something

hard, his breath knocked from
him like he'd been gut-punched
by a boxer.

CHAPTER SIX

Catching his breath Trev noticed
the air was fresh. He was outside,
helmet and axe gone, and
kneeling on grass. Beyond him
was the hospital. And standing in
the doorway, dressed head to toe

in black, its face hidden behind a metallic mask, was a cloaked figure the size of a giant. It moved towards him and, a stride short of stamping on Trev, stopped dead. From behind its cloak the figure pulled out the helmet and axe, held them out for Trev.

Trev took the helmet. It slipped easily over his head. Through the visor he gazed once more on the horror. Where the hospital had been was now the beast. What had been bricks and mortar was now flesh and bone, a vast and awful thing so far beyond all reason and possibility that Trev couldn't take it in. And it was howling now, dying.

The figure pointed at the beast and a sound came from the other side of its mask. A wet gurgling, like a drain sucking a bath dry. But words were in the wetness.

"Finish it."

It held out the axe, only now it was a silvery thing, both slender and terrible, with an edge keen enough to splice time.

With a nod, Trev roared, raised the axe, and charged at the beast. The first blow shattered the door into splinters, smashed teeth into shards of ivory, split tentacles in two. The second killed a window, pierced an eye. But Trev didn't stop. Down the axe came, again and again, until it was over and the beast was dead, the tentacles in pieces around his feet.

"You killed it," the figure said, joining Trev. "Good."

Trev raised the helmet's visor

and went to reply, but a sharp
stab to his skull made him yelp.
The next few seconds were filled
with a pain of the hottest fire and
Trev knew that the helmet was
sewing itself to his skin. He pulled
at it, but the thing was fused to
his head. Then a voice spoke to
Trev from inside his mind. The
language was not his own, yet he
understood every word.

"You passed the test. You're one
of us now," it said. "Shepherd."

"I don't get what you mean,"
Trev replied.

"Protect the flock. Hunt the parasite."

The figure raised a hand to point at the creature that had once been the hospital. Then, almost as though information was being downloaded into his brain, Trev understood. He saw pictures of other worlds, civilisations. Hunting grounds where the creatures went to feed.

"I am Shepherd," said Trev. "I will protect my flock."

Something sparked in his brain. A scent or signal he wasn't sure, but it told him to move. It also systematically shut down every other bit of his memory.

And Trev was dead.

* * * * *

Shepherd turned and followed the
signal. Some time later, hours or
days — it didn't matter, a house
came into view, a car in the drive,
a man at the door.

Shepherd snapped his visor
down. The house shimmered
like a heat wave and the image
collapsed.

Shepherd stared at the beast,
at the awful thing in its mouth
screaming at him. Then, with the
shaft of the axe tight in his hand,
and the knowledge that he was
doing good by killing the beast,

he attacked. The axe rising and
falling, rising and falling, until
everything was

Blood red.
Torn flesh.
Red blood.

ABOUT THE AUTHOR

The idea for this stemmed from the way animals use camouflage to catch their prey. That, and the fact that we humans are basically top dog.

So I got to thinking, what if we weren't, but just didn't know? What if there was a creature out there so well camouflaged that it's been munching on us for millennia without us ever knowing?

With that being the case I had to work out how such a thing would stay secret for so long, what it would camouflage itself as. And it made sense, to me anyway, that it would try to be where we always are, without us ever knowing.

Thus you end up with this awful creation of a creature that feeds on humans and disguises itself as the places in which we live. And we only find out when it's too late.

For this to work, though, it had to have a central figure, someone who's seen the creatures and survived. But of course no one's going to believe such a story are they?

So Trev ends up in a secure medical hospital of sorts, harassed by the staff to essentially admit to murdering his family, and then another creature comes for him. It's a weird, creepy, dark story. And I hope you like it.

David Gatward, July 2012

www.davidgatward.co.uk

Get in touch with David through his website.

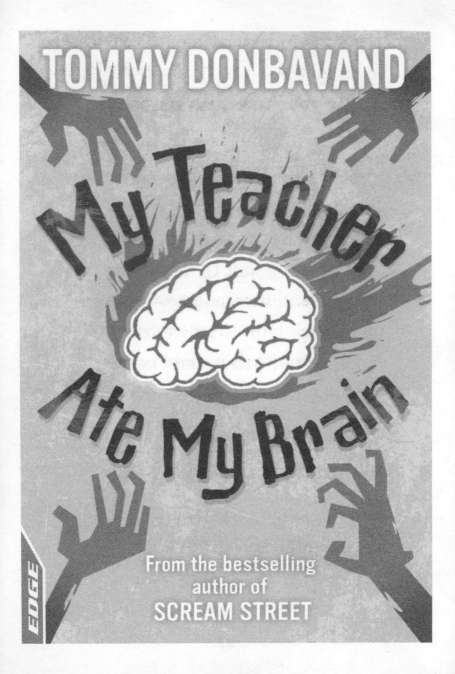

TOMMY DONBAVAND

My Teacher
Ate My Brain

From the bestselling
author of
SCREAM STREET

EDGE

If you enjoyed reading **BLOOD HOUSE**,
you might also like My Teacher Ate My Brain,
by Tommy Donbavand.

Miss Edwards had always smelled
like a spring day — all honey and
strawberries.

Now she smells of rotten meat.

Of terror. Of death.

Josh's camping trip to a remote
Welsh island has gone wrong.

Horribly wrong.

www.tommydonbavand.com

Buy online at
www.franklinwatts.co.uk
978 1 4451 1467 5 paperback
978 1 4451 1470 5 eBook

Turn over to read an extract from
My Teacher Ate My Brain:

Her hair was matted with blood
and lumps of grey that I knew
had to be one of my classmate's
brains. I had to get away.

Suddenly, my foot caught in
a hole and a lightning bolt of
pain shot up from my ankle as
it twisted violently to one side.
I fell, face first, into the sand,
and for a second I almost gave
up. I almost lay there and let Miss
Edwards finish me off. But then I
realised I was clutching something
in my hand and I lifted my head
to see what it was.

I was still holding the spatula Mr Blake had handed me ready to cook sausages on the barbecue. I watched in fascination as the moonlight glinted on its shining, metal surface.

GLARK!

I flipped myself over onto my back at the sound — just in time to see Miss Edwards's twisted face plunge down, teeth aimed squarely for my throat. I lashed out with the spatula as hard as I could, and caught her in the side of the face. The blow was enough

to knock her to one side — but
also enough to snap the head
from the spatula. Now all I had
was a jagged metal stick in my
hand. And that was probably what
saved me.

Miss Edwards loomed back over
me, a mixture of her blood and
saliva spattering down on my
cheeks like warm, sticky rain.
Her eyes — milky and unfocussed
— gazed down at me hungrily.
And then I knew what I had to
do. Placing the heel of my hand
against the bottom of the

spatula's handle, I pushed the sharp end as hard as I could into one of her eyes. Her eyeball popped — I actually heard it — and then all resistance was gone.

The metal spear sank deep into Miss Edwards's brain and, with a final groan, her lifeless body slumped down on top of me. I turned my head to one side — partly to catch my breath and partly so that I didn't have to look at what I'd just done.

Want to find out if Miss Edwards is really dead? Get hold of a copy of My Teacher Ate My Brain today!

Also available from EDGE.
CRIME TEAM adventures by the 2Steves,
where YOU crack the case!

978 0 7496 9283 4 pb
978 1 4451 0843 8 eBook

978 0 7496 9284 1 pb
978 1 4451 0844 5 eBook

978 0 7496 9286 5 pb
978 1 4451 0845 2 eBook

978 0 7496 9285 8 pb
978 1 4451 0846 9 eBook

PREGNANCY
+ drug misuse

Edited by
Catherine Siney SRN RM

With
Peter Carey
Neil Lloyd-Knapman
Lyn Matthews
Clive Morrison
Sue Ruben
Ben Shaw
Colette Sparey
Steve Walkinshaw

BfM **Books** *for* **Midwives**

OXFORD AUCKLAND BOSTON JOHANNESBURG MELBOURNE NEW DELHI

Books for Midwives
An imprint of Butterworth-Heinemann
Linacre House, Jordan Hill, Oxford OX2 8DP
225 Wildwood Avenue, Woburn, MA 01801-2041
A division of Reed Educational and Professional Publishing Ltd

℞ A member of the Reed Elsevier plc group

First published 1995 (previously titled *The Pregnant Drug Addict*)
Second edition 1999
Reprinted 2001

ISBN 1 898507 77 5

British Library Cataloguing in Publication Data
A catalogue record for this book is available from the British Library.

For information on all Butterworth-Heinemann publications visit our
website at www.bh.com

Printed in Great Britain by Athenæum Press Ltd, Gateshead, Tyne & Wear

INTRODUCTION

This book, now updated and with an extra chapter on the effects on the child, has been put together as an introduction, for health care professionals, to the problems of drug dependence in women who become pregnant. Many drugs, both illicit and prescribed, are abused, and there may be many effects on the woman during pregnancy and on the baby both before and after birth.

Approximately 100 known drug dependent women are delivered in the Liverpool Women's Hospital annually and a liaison service for these women has been available since 1990.

In 1990 I looked around for a book which would give me an overview of the subject and could not find one. I wanted to know about the history of drug abuse, where the systems for drug treatment programmes came from and the effects of drugs on the fetus and neonate as well as on the woman. I hope that this book will at least go part of the way to explaining these and other points. The people I asked to contribute all have extensive experience in their field and I felt that it would be good to have the benefit of their experience to give a broad picture of this extremely complex subject. Some of the chapters will overlap but this will allow them to be read on their own.

Acknowledgements

I would like to thank all the staff of Liverpool Women's Hospital, the staff of the statutory and voluntary drug agencies of Liverpool, Sefton and South Knowsley, and all my colleagues from outside agencies for all their help and support since the service began in March 1990.

Special thanks to Sue Ruben, Clive Morrison, Steve Walkinshaw, Mervyn Kidd, Lydia Moore, Julie Riley and John Siney.

Chapter 1

AN OVERVIEW

Catherine Siney

Catherine Siney is the specialist midwife liaison at the Liverpool Women's Hospital. She coordinates the obstetric and gynaecology services for women who are drug and/or alcohol dependent or who are HIV or hepatitis positive. She began the service in 1990 and is responsible for the training of all staff around the issues of drugs, HIV and hepatitis. In 1993 the service was cited as an example of good practice in 'The A-Z of Quality' NHS Executive. She was the midwife member of the working groups who assisted the ENB to develop 'Substance use and misuse: guidelines for good practice in training of nurses, midwives and health visitors' in 1996. She has published many papers and articles in national and international journals and regularly speaks at conferences and seminars at home and abroad.

In the nineteenth century opiate use was widespread in Britain, as well as in North America and parts of Europe. Opium and laudanum were used by the middle classes for self-medication, literary and bohemian circles indulged for experimentation and the working classes used them as intoxicants and aids to physical labour. During the course of the industrial revolution there were public health concerns about workers' use of opiates and also about the practice of 'infant doping' with remedies such as 'Soothing Syrup' and 'Mothers' Quietness'. In the late nineteenth century there were vivid accounts of opium dens in the East End of London which led to further concerns and anxieties about the moral welfare of the working classes.

In the eighteenth and early nineteenth centuries the approach became more medically orientated. The Pharmacy Act 1868 restricted the sale of morphine and opium by pharmacists and prohibited their sale by grocers and general stores; in 1908 the Poisons and Pharmacy Act regulated the sale of patent medicines. Medical practitioners made various attempts to extend the provisions of the Inebriates Act in 1888 to cover those who became dependent on opiates, but failed. The Inebriates Act allowed for voluntary detention of 'habitual drunkards' and 'inebriates'. However the Lunacy Act of 1890 was also sometimes applied to drug addicts. This Act allowed for a form of guardianship for patients deemed incapable of managing their affairs and property. In 1913 the Mental Deficiency Act defined any sedative, narcotic or stimulant drug as an 'intoxicant'; this then allowed for people who were deemed 'moral imbeciles' to be confined within an institution or placed under guardianship. British opinion was divided in 1914; addiction was seen as either a medical problem to be treated or a vice to be controlled through penal sanctions. During World War I (1914-1918) there was great concern about the spread of cocaine and a regulation was introduced under the Defence of the Realms Act (DORA 40B) which prohibited the possession of cocaine unless it had been supplied on prescription. The Dangerous Drugs Acts of 1920 and 1923 made possession of opiates and cocaine illegal unless supplied by a doctor, and the Home Secretary was authorised to regulate the manufacture, distribution and sale of these substances.

These Acts brought addiction into the criminal model of action but the Rolleston Committee (Departmental Committee on Morphine and Heroin Addiction) was established in 1924 by the Ministry of Health 'to consider and advise on the circumstances, if any, in which the supply of morphine and heroin... to persons suffering from addiction to those drugs may be regarded as medically advisable and as to the precautions which it is advisable that medical practitioners administering or prescribing morphine or heroin should adopt for the avoidance of abuse'. The recommendations of the committee were that the prescription of heroin and morphine to certain classes of addicts was to be deemed a 'legitimate medical treatment' and that control of prescribing practices was to be by professional self-regulation through a medical panel. However, unauthorised possession of certain substances remained a criminal offence.

The Interdepartmental Committee on Drug Addiction was convened in 1958 to review existing policy and concluded that addiction to dangerous drugs was still a small problem. It was reconvened in 1962 and in 1964 there was great public concern about the use of amphetamines ('pep pills' and 'purple hearts') and cannabis among young people. The number of known heroin addicts had also risen from 47 to 328 over a five year period – 1959 to 1964 – and the total number of known addicts rose from 260 in 1954 to 753 in 1964. The committee recommended tighter controls on the supply of drugs to addicts, these controls to take the form of a system of notification, to a central authority, by doctors, of any unregistered addicts with whom they came into professional contact. Specialist drug treatment centres were to be established, at least in the London area, with only the staff there retaining the right to prescribe heroin and cocaine to drug addicts, and these treatment centres should have powers to detain addicts for compulsory treatment if this was felt to be necessary. All the recommendations except the last were put into the Dangerous Drugs Act of 1967, and subsequently in April of 1968 regulations were introduced that prohibited ordinary medical practitioners from prescribing heroin and cocaine to addicts.

A number of Acts control non-medical drug use. The Misuse of Drugs Act 1971 controls certain drugs by placing them into classes and schedules. It defines the things it is illegal to do with these controlled drugs and outlines penalties for these offences.

Controlled drugs are divided into three classes:

- **Class A drugs** include cocaine, heroin and other opiates, ecstasy, LSD and other hallucinogens.

- **Class B drugs** include amphetamines and other strong stimulants, barbiturates, cannabis and codeine. Any class B drug prepared for injection becomes a class A drug.

- **Class C drugs** include benzodiazepines, barbiturates, mild stimulants and distalgesics.

There are five schedules for controlled drugs; these regulations allow the government to authorise the supply, possession and import of controlled drugs for medical or scientific purposes.

The Road Traffic Act 1972 makes it an offence to drive, to attempt to drive or to be in charge of a motor vehicle when unfit through drink or drugs. The 1991 Road Traffic Act added the offence of causing death by careless driving when under the influence of drink or drugs.

In the 1970s clinics transferred patients from heroin (which was injected) onto injectable methadone as a substitute, and then moved towards prescription of oral methadone as treatment in either detoxification or maintenance regimes. In 1983 there was a 42% increase in the number of addicts notified to the Home Office, almost entirely confined to heroin misuse. In 1984 there were 5190 addicts receiving methadone in the United Kingdom, but by 1987 this number had increased to 9763. (Methadone was the first completely synthetic opiate-like drug. It was developed in Germany during World War 2 and appeared in America in the late 1940s.)

The heroin epidemic which emerged in the 1980s was associated with the arrival of cheap and plentiful heroin from Southwest Asia. Heroin misuse became a serious problem in many towns and cities in the North of England and in Scotland, where heroin had previously been largely unknown. Research papers began to be published detailing a sharp increase in heroin misuse in places like Glasgow, Edinburgh, Liverpool, Sheffield, Carlisle and Manchester. The scale was enormous; for example, in the Wirral peninsula (Cheshire) alone detailed prevalence estimates indicated that there were some 5000 regular heroin users in 1987 when there had been fewer than a hundred people known to be using opiates in 1980. In one town in the Wirral peninsula, where the problem was particularly severe, as many as 8.6% of the 16 to 24-year-old age group were known heroin users. There was a tendency for heroin misuse to be associated with high levels of unemployment and other forms of social deprivation. This experience in the 1980s confirmed the earlier tendency in the United States for heroin misuse to be associated with areas of urban deprivation. The realisation that the Southwest Asian imported 'brown' heroin could be 'smoked' (the practice of 'chasing the dragon') helped to accelerate the growth of the heroin habit among people for whom self-injection would have proved a barrier. In areas such as Merseyside and Manchester, 'chasing the dragon' became the dominant route of administration.

In 1984 a ministerial sub-committee was appointed by the government, who were alarmed at the increase in heroin misuse. The following year a strategy document called 'Tackling Drug Misuse' was issued. Action on five main fronts was proposed:

- reducing supplies from abroad
- making enforcement even more effective
- maintaining effective deterrents and tighter domestic controls
- developing prevention
- improving treatment and rehabilitation.

The two broad initiatives on the domestic front were the enhancement of health education programmes and a Central Funding Initiative (CFI) to improve services for drug misusers. The CFI led to the development of community based services which have played a crucial role in limiting the spread of human immunodeficiency virus (HIV). These services at local level contain a range of advice and treatment options, and remain a key part of overall HIV and drug misuse prevention.

Since 1985 a number of papers, reports and reviews looking at the drug misuse problem have been published. These include:

Across the Divide – Building community partnerships to tackle drug misuse. Department of Health, February 1994

The Criminal Justice System and the care of Drug Users. North West Regional Health Authority, March 1996

The Task Force to Review the Effectiveness of Treatment Services for Drug Misusers. Final report (an independent survey), May 1996

Children and Young People –substance misuse services – the substance of young needs. Health Advisory Service Thematic Review, 1996

The NHS Drug Advisory Service – services for people who misuse substances – a review England and Wales 1986–1993, December 1996

Tackling Drugs Together – a strategy for England, May 1995

The Task Force to Review Service for Drug Misusers. Report of Independent Review of Drug Treatment Services in England. Department of Health, November 1996

Statistics gathering

In March 1994 the Department of Health issued the first bulletin in a series containing aggregate information on those drug misusers attending services for problem drug misusers in England. It covered a six month period and included new attenders rather than people already in contact with such services. The information, which now reaches the Department of Health via the Regional Health Authority Drug Misuse Databases, includes the age group and sex of the person, the types of drugs misused, whether the drug is injected or not and the type of agency contacted.

In 1993 a survey was undertaken to determine the prevalence of drug misuse in pregnancy and to describe the services provided by maternity services for drug misusers.[1] A postal questionnaire was sent to 213 maternity units in England and Wales, asking about the extent of their involvement with pregnant drug misusers, the services offered, the availability of liaison with drug treatment agencies and the policies on health care for neonates. The response rate was 89.3% (191). There was an estimated number of 568 deliveries to drug misusers in a 12-month period. Only 29% (57) of maternity units had formal links with local drug agencies and 52% (100) automatically convened social care child service discussions. Fifty-seven percent (109) routinely admitted babies of drug misusing mothers to special care baby units and, although hepatitis B screening was offered to women in 73% (146) of the units, only 68% (129) offered hepatitis B prophylaxis to the babies of women found to be infected in pregnancy. The results of the survey showed that local health purchasers needed to undertake needs assessment to ensure that discriminatory practices were not deterring women from seeking help.

The importance of effective antenatal care

The World Health Organisation (WHO) review of antenatal care published in 1992[2] stressed the importance of effective antenatal care for the future health and wellbeing of mothers and children. Education about pregnancy and childbirth should be started at an early age. The importance of good general health and planned pregnancy cannot be too heavily emphasised. Alcohol and tobacco in pregnancy are known to be detrimental to the health of the mother and of the developing fetus, and are associated with premature birth and low birthweight.[3] Misuse of other drugs, for example opiates, is also associated with low birthweight and premature birth.[4] Encouraging women who are dependent on drugs to tell the maternity services is very important – it gives them the chance to ask questions and allows healthcare professionals to offer them choices. It empowers them, it gives them a chance to take control of an aspect of their life. Midwives must strive to find patterns of care that suit all women, not just the educationally and financially advantaged sections of society. Care should be holistic, that is, it must consider not only physical but also social and financial needs.

While pregnancy will be a time of happiness for many women, particularly those having their first child, it can also be a time of great anxiety. They may worry about how parenthood and the responsibilities it will bring will change their lives. Financial or housing problems may add to these anxieties. For the woman who is dependent on drugs, all these anxieties are added to her addiction and, where illegal drugs are involved, the risky lifestyle that goes with it. Drug-taking women, especially those using opiates, may have menstrual irregularities;[5] it could therefore also be a huge shock for them to find themselves pregnant and this combination of shock and anxiety may make it difficult for some women to give up drugs and change their lifestyle. Many feel guilt about using drugs when pregnant but still are unable to give up their addiction. They may also fear, even when unjustified, that the unborn child or their existing children will be taken away if health or social workers find out about their drug use, and that they will be stigmatised when they go into hospital. It is vitally important that women who are drug dependent are looked upon by maternity services as pregnant women who misuse drugs rather than drug misusing women who are pregnant. If women are leading an illegal lifestyle then they may have lied to almost everyone they have come into contact with and that is why continuity of personnel is essential – this allows a relationship to develop and helps to engender an atmosphere of trust. Another essential is that maternity service personnel should be aware of their attitudes towards women who misuse drugs and should ensure that negative attitudes do not spoil the chance of a good relationship. If women are discouraged from attending for antenatal care because of the treatment they receive, neither they nor their babies will receive the care they need, and studies in the United States from 1969 to 1974 showed that illness in babies born to drug-dependent women could be directly related to the amount of antenatal care they received.[5] Questioning for all women in the antenatal period should not simply be about the mother's general health and any drugs used, including tobacco and alcohol; the opportunity should also be used to educate mothers about the risks to the fetus associated with all drugs taken during pregnancy. In this way, drug use in the woman is seen as an obstetric/paediatric concern, rather than a moral one.

Identification of women who are drug dependent is of benefit not only to the mother and the fetus, but also to the staff. Women who are cared for by staff who are not visibly disapproving of them or their lifestyle will find that the problems that they expect to experience as in-patients often do not materialise. Another important plus is that any social service concerns may be addressed before the women are admitted to hospital and any decisions needed can be made before the birth.

It is important that women are informed about the proven risks of the drugs they use, and that maternity and drug prescribing services work together to reduce the overall amount of drugs used during pregnancy in order to reduce the incidence of low birthweight and the effects of neonatal withdrawal from drugs.

Confidentiality and child protection

The confidentiality clause (in the Code of Professional Conduct UKCC 1992[6]) says that information obtained in the course of professional practice shall be respected and that such information cannot be disclosed without the consent of the patient/client, or a person entitled to act on his/her behalf, except where disclosure is required by law or by the order of a court or is necessary to the public interest. A breach of confidentiality occurs if anyone, deliberately or by accident, gives information which has been obtained in the course of professional practice to a third party without the consent of the patient/client. The 'public interest' is taken to mean the interest of an individual, of groups of individuals or of society as a whole, and would encompass matters such as serious crime, child abuse and drug trafficking. (Trafficking – to deal or bargain in something that should not be the subject of trade. The Concise Oxford Dictionary of Current English.)

There is no statutory right to confidentiality, but there is also nothing to stop an aggrieved individual from bringing a common law case before a civil court alleging breach of confidentiality and seeking financial recompense. Information shared with other professionals in the health and social work fields is shared in the belief that this is in the interest of the patient/client. Legislation covering data protection and its associated codes is not intended to prevent the exchange of information between professional staff who share the care of the patient/client. It is the duty of the practitioner to ensure, as far as is possible, that information shared is in strict professional confidence and for a specific purpose and in all cases she/he must be able to justify the decision. It may be appropriate for a practitioner to consult with their professional organisation.

Even taking this into account, the safety of a child is paramount. If a child is either harmed or at risk of 'significant harm' then confidentiality can be legally breached. If you as a health care professional are unsure about this then you should discuss this with the person in your organisation responsible for child protection issues.

Contrary to what some health care professionals believe it is possible to be a parent and a drug misuser. The report 'Drug using parents – policy guidelines for inter-agency working' by the Standing Conference on Drug Abuse (SCODA) and the Local Government Drugs Forum (LGDF) 1997, makes it clear that drug misuse in itself is not sufficient reason to separate mother and child. The Children Act 1989 contains many principles and provisions, but an overriding principle is that in all court proceedings the welfare of the child will be paramount. In deciding what happens to a child the court has to consider the wishes of the child (in the light of age and understanding). If a local authority wishes to separate a parent from a child they have to show that the child's interest will be better served with separation and they have to demonstrate that the child would come to significant harm if left in his/her environment, and that the harm is attributable to the care being given to the child.

'Significant harm' is defined thus: 'where the question of whether harm suffered by the child is significant turns on the child's health or development, (this) shall be compared with that which could be reasonably expected of a similar child'.[7]

The 1997 report suggests that maternity services should identify one person to be responsible for coordinating care and liaison with all other relevant agencies. It also suggests that regular contact is made between the agencies to ensure that existing problems are looked at and potential difficulties are avoided or reduced.

Effects of drugs on pregnancy and the neonate

It is generally accepted that drugs should be prescribed in pregnancy only if the benefit to the mother outweighs the risk to the fetus. During the first trimester drugs may produce congenital malformations, that is they may be teratogenic, and during the second and third trimesters they may affect growth and functional development. Women may not be in contact with any agency which can tell them about the possible risks to their baby if they take drugs, including tobacco and alcohol, during pregnancy. It is also important to remember that many of the obstetric problems commonly associated with illicit drug use are also associated with social deprivation and poor health and nutrition. However, in Liverpool we found that things were not necessarily as bad as they seemed. The results of a retrospective case-control study comparing the outcomes of pregnancy of 103 opiate-dependent women who were on a methadone programme, and who received regular antenatal care, with women who were matched by age, parity and postal code who were not known to be drug misusers, showed that apart from an increased risk of prematurity and a reduction in birthweight the outcomes were broadly similar.[4]

The effects of drugs in pregnancy are discussed more fully in Chapter 5, 'Obstetric problems for drug users'.

Intravenous injection of drugs presents the risk of both local and systemic infection (see the chapters on medical problems and HIV).

It is important to remember that there is a difference between drug misuse and drug dependence. Drug misuse, which is broadly equivalent to 'drug abuse' and 'problem drug taking', denotes drug taking which is hazardous or harmful and is unsanctioned by professional or cultural standards. Drug dependence is a term used to describe the altered physical and psychological state which results in disturbed physical and mental functioning when the drug is abruptly discontinued. It is broadly equivalent to 'drug addiction'. However, not all drug misusers are drug dependent.[8] Generally drugs on which women are dependent are likely to cause problems for the baby when it is withdrawn from the source, that is, after birth. Symptoms of withdrawal vary in strength and effect, dependent probably on the condition of the baby after birth.[9] This would explain the wide variation in symptoms seen even when women have taken broadly similar amounts of illicit drugs. Mild symptoms may include sneezing, yawning, poor feeding, tremors when disturbed and loose stools; severe symptoms may include convulsions, tremors when undisturbed, nonstop high-pitched cry, sleeping less than an hour after a good feed, watery stools and projectile vomiting. Mild symptoms, when the baby can be comforted and continues to feed, will probably not require treatment, but treatment will be necessary if the baby becomes dehydrated, has convulsions or its agitation cannot be comforted. Treatment should make the baby comfortable enough to take a feed and settle down afterwards. The aim should be to comfort the baby until the effects of drug withdrawal have subsided, and to enable him/her to feed normally. In 1985 Strang and Moran of the Manchester Regional Drug Dependence Unit recommended that opiate withdrawal symptoms should be treated by giving an opiate and then weaning down but not sedating the child; if the maternal addiction is to barbiturates then the baby should be weaned off with phenobarbitone and if the maternal addiction is to benzodiazepines then the baby should be treated with diazepam. In Liverpool we have been treating severe opiate withdrawal symptoms in the neonate by giving morphine sulphate orally and reducing it 24 hours after the baby becomes more settled over a period of days (see Chapter 6, 'Maternal drug use: consequences for the child'). We have been doing this since June 1993 and have found that these babies have been made comfortable without being sedated and have consequently been able to feed. We have also been able to formulate a policy for the discharge of drug dependent women and their babies. We found from our data that babies who did not exhibit severe symptoms by 72 hours of age did not develop them later. Consequently nowadays they are discharged after three or four days, even if they have mild symptoms, if there are no medical reasons to keep them in hospital and provided that the mother is happy with this. Although there is no easy way to predict withdrawal symptoms in neonates, in our eight-year experience of over 500 live births in the Liverpool Women's Hospital we have found that, generally, full term healthy babies can cope well with withdrawal from quite large amounts of drugs, but smaller weaker babies find it difficult to cope with even relatively small amounts of drugs. It would appear that problems with withdrawal depend on many variables including gestation and weight at delivery, the amount of opiates the mother has taken and when (in relation to labour) and the general condition of the baby. It would be easy to say that a large amount of drugs taken guarantees withdrawal symptoms that require treatment in the neonate, and a small amount carries no risk, but this has not been the case in Liverpool. Matters can also be complicated by other drugs the mother may or may not admit to taking, and consequently discharge may be delayed. Babies who have not exhibited obvious signs of withdrawal postnatally have often had episodes of distress in labour, shown by either meconium-stained liquor or a sub-optimal tracing on the cardiotocograph, and may even have had an operative or instrumental delivery because of 'fetal distress' and this may have occurred due to drug withdrawal in the fetus during the course of labour. All drug-dependent women who come into contact with the maternity/drug liaison service are told of the risks of neonatal drug withdrawal both during pregnancy and after birth, and occasionally this has influenced a woman's decision to stop illicit drug use and also to reduce her methadone prescription in order to help the baby. A reduction in overall drug use should also include tobacco and alcohol, the risks of which are well documented.

I think it is important to keep neonatal withdrawal in perspective – to ensure that babies who require treatment are given the right treatment, but equally that babies are not given treatment unnecessarily. Many babies exhibit some of the minor symptoms attributed to drug withdrawal for all sorts of reasons, and they are not treated or sedated. Staff must be sure that symptoms are related to drug withdrawal before treatment is commenced, and that any reason other than drug withdrawal is excluded in the baby of a drug dependent woman.

The use of score charts for observation of neonatal withdrawal is problematic, often because there is a risk of subjectivity. Many charts ask the observer if a symptom is mild or severe and allocates a score to it. Scores are added up and treatment is initiated when a certain score is reached. If an observer has never cared for an infant of a drug dependent mother, can they decide on the severity of a symptom? If more than one observer is used over a period of time then how accurate is the observation? If an observer has certain views about drug misuse and pregnancy could this influence the score? It would probably be more accurate to assess the wellbeing and need for treatment by looking at whether the baby is feeding and whether, even if agitated, he/she can be comforted enough to settle between feeds. Mothers should be supported in the care of their baby so that their guilt and stress, and even the stress of the staff, do not influence the decision to treat the baby.

This subject is dealt with at length in Chapter 6, 'Maternal drug use: consequences for the child'.

Screening in pregnancy

In July 1998, the National Screening Committee of the Department of Health recommended that all pregnant women should be offered antenatal screening for hepatitis B by April 2000 at the latest, and that the appropriate immunisation should take place of babies born to mothers found to be infected.

Hepatitis B infection can be transmitted from infected mothers to their babies at or around the time of birth (perinatal transmission). Babies acquiring infection at this time have a high risk of becoming chronic carriers of the virus. Such carriers, as well as being infectious to others, are at an increased risk of developing chronic liver disease and some will die prematurely from cirrhosis or hepatocellular carcinoma (primary liver cancer). The development of the carrier state after perinatal transmission can be prevented in around 90-95% of cases by appropriate immunisation, starting at birth.

Women who have a past or present history of intravenous drug use can be offered screening for hepatitis C as well as B, provided that follow-up care is available for them and their babies. (See Chapter 7, 'Hepatitis B, pregnancy and the drug user'.)

In April 1998 an Intercollegiate Working Party made some recommendations for enhancing voluntary confidential HIV testing in pregnancy. Currently about 300 infants are born to HIV infected women each year in the UK. There is now clear evidence that transmission of HIV from an infected mother to her child can be greatly reduced by interventions such as anti-retroviral treatment in pregnancy and in the perinatal period, and the avoidance of breastfeeding.

The document 'Reducing Mother to Child Transmission of HIV Infection in the United Kingdom' (1998) recommended that all pregnant women should receive appropriate information on HIV infection and its vertical transmission. HIV testing should be universally available, but it should be obligatory in areas of high prevalence, such as Greater London, to offer and recommend HIV testing to all women receiving antenatal care.

In 1996 epidemiological information showed the prevalence of HIV among pregnant women in London to be 1 in 520, and elsewhere in the UK to be 1 in 5700. (See Chapter 8, 'HIV, pregnancy and the drug user'.)

Fetal rights versus maternal rights

Over the last few years a number of cases have arisen concerning fetal rights. There appears to be a trend to view maternal rights and fetal rights as antagonistic. The law relating to consent to treatment by the mentally competent adult is clear. If a patient/client refuses consent to treatment then any touching of that person is trespass. If the patient/client is unconscious then a doctor could act in an emergency to save her/his life as part of the doctor's duty of care to that patient. Consent does not need to be in writing to be legally effective, it can be given orally. The fact that a patient/client has come into hospital does not, however, imply consent to treatment.

A pregnant woman addicted to illicit drugs, alcohol or smoking tobacco, which was endangering the wellbeing of the fetus, would not be committing a criminal offence under the Infant Life (Preservation) Act 1929 unless there was evidence of intention to bring about an abortion or to destroy a child capable of being born alive. The 1929 Act makes it a criminal offence for 'any person who, with intent to destroy the life of a child capable of being born alive, by any wilful act, causes a child to die before it has an existence independent of its mother'. The only defence is preservation of the life of the mother. The Congenital Disabilities Act 1976 does not apply either. This Act was passed to give to the child born disabled as a result of a negligent act prior to its birth the right to sue in respect of that negligent act. It seems that provided health care professionals give all relevant information to a mother, and also act in accordance with what is established practice, then the health care professionals cannot be deemed as negligent in law.

In 1986 a woman in California faced criminal charges arising from the death of her son. Thomas was born with massive brain damage. His mother had started to haemorrhage slightly, on 23 November 1985 at 07.30 hours, but did not seek aid until 20.00 hours that evening despite being told in her pregnancy that she had a placenta praevia condition, that she should not take unprescribed drugs, that she should rest, refrain from sexual intercourse and should seek medical aid if she started to haemorrhage. However, after starting to haemorrhage slightly she and her husband took some amphetamines and had sexual intercourse. She began to bleed more heavily and contractions began at 14.00 hours. Thomas was born on 23 November 1985 with traces of amphetamine and marijuana in his blood; he died on 1 January 1987. His mother was charged under a section of the misdemeanour criminal code 1926 (USA). The statute makes it a crime for a parent to 'wilfully omit, without excuse, to furnish necessary medical attendance for her child'. Under this statute a fetus is deemed a person. This statute was designed to be used by women who seek support payments from husbands who have deserted them. The charges against Thomas's mother were dropped in March 1987 when the judge ruled that the 1926 law did not apply.

In 1989 Melanie Green was charged with involuntary manslaughter and supplying drugs to a minor after her daughter Bianca was born with severe oxygen deprivation and cocaine was found in her urine. When Cassandra Gethers gave birth to her second cocaine-affected child she was charged with child abuse and her baby was placed in foster care.

In the same year, Brenda Vaughn was arrested for cheque fraud and a routine urine test contained cocaine. Since it was her first offence and she was pregnant the prosecutor recommended probation, but the judge sentenced her to four months' imprisonment, which ensured her baby was born drug-free.

In 1990, US attorney Lynn Bremer delivered a baby with cocaine in her urine. She was charged with delivery of drugs to her new-born baby. The child was taken into temporary custody. Bremer went through a treatment programme and regained custody of her daughter.

In 1994 Jason Allen was found dead in his cot when he was two months old. Methamphetamine was found in his urine. His mother was accused of killing him by breastfeeding him after snorting the drug. She was found guilty of child endangerment but the jury failed to agree on a charge of second-degree murder. She went to jail.

Also in 1994 the Royal College of Obstetricians and Gynaecologists and the American College of Obstetricians and Gynaecologists agreed that pregnant women should not be subject to coerced intervention.

In 1996 Deborah Zimmerman from Wisconsin, USA, was charged with attempting to murder her fetus by drinking alcohol throughout her pregnancy. The baby girl, Meagan, born at term, weighed 1,985g and had mild fetal alcohol syndrome (FAS). She had a blood alcohol almost twice the legal adult level for intoxication.

Priscilla Smith, head of New York City's Center for Reproductive and Policy Law, asks: 'But can a fetus really have rights? And can a mother violate those rights by delivering drugs and alcohol to a fetus via the placenta?'

This advocacy group has fought many of the 200 cases that have spread across 30 US states in the past few years. Americans have long been divided over reproductive rights. Ms Smith says: 'It is a legal minefield and the other concern is where the government intervention ends. Now it is drugs and alcohol, but will they eventually target mothers who simply smoke cigarettes?'

Arguments about mandatory treatment policies have gone on for a number of years in America, and although both the American Medical Association and the American College of Obstetricians and Gynaecologists oppose mandatory treatment, in 1992 mandatory treatment policies existed in several states. Poor women and those from ethnic minorities are most often affected by them. A study of pregnant women in Florida by Dr Ira Chasnoff, Head of the Association for Perinatal Addiction Research, found that 14% of black women and 15.4% of white women used drugs, but ten black women were reported for every white woman. The American Civil Liberties Union argues that forcing pregnant women to undergo treatment strips them of their rights.[10] In 81% of the cases taken to court when a woman has refused treatment, the woman concerned has been a minority woman with a white male physician. These statistics have been seen as a worrying trend by Lori Andrews, a research fellow of the American Bar Foundation and a senior scholar at the University of Chicago Center for Medical Ethics. Women are usually charged with delivering drugs to a minor or under child abuse laws. Interestingly, in cases where women have been beaten by their partners and miscarried no action was taken against the man.[11]

There are also polarised views in this country about the rights of the fetus. To date, the debate in the UK has largely focused on the abortion issue.

There is a difference between child protection and fetal protection. When pregnant, a mentally competent woman has the right to decide what to do with her own body, even when what she wants is against the advice of health care professionals.

Barrister Barbara Hewson, who has been involved in several high-profile cases, including one in which the right of a woman to refuse a Caesarean section was challenged, asks: 'Will women be compelled by courts to refrain from drinking alcohol or smoking cigarettes because it may damage their unborn fetus?'

We know that drugs should be prescribed in pregnancy only if the benefits to the mother outweigh the risks to the baby. But since half of pregnancies are unplanned, some women will have been prescribed and will have taken drugs before they realised that they were pregnant, including women with chronic illnesses who need anticonvulsants or antidepressants. In these situations we seldom hear a discussion about the rights of the fetus or hear talk of weighing the risks and benefits to both mother and child.

But if a woman is dependent on an illicit drug, such as heroin, or is prescribed methadone, her physical and psychological dependence on opiates is viewed as a matter of choice. The view often expressed is that now that she is pregnant the woman will stop taking drugs because this is better for the baby. If she does not stop then apparently she thinks the wellbeing of the baby is less important than her own.

Surely, people argue, the rights of the baby are disregarded if a drug-dependent woman continues to use heroin or benzodiazepines. The baby has a right to the best possible start in life. If a woman does not put the baby first during pregnancy, should we not have concern about her care of that child postnatally?

Health care professionals need to be very sure that their concerns about fetal wellbeing are rooted in concerns about health risks and not moral ones.

Of course this does not mean that parental drug dependence/use should be ignored, but it should be looked at as a health concern first and then put into the context of risk to a child's wellbeing along with any other risks that there may be, e.g. housing problems, money problems, domestic violence issues.

Information about drugs

Comprehensive information about drugs can be obtained from the Drug Notes series of booklets produced by the Institute for the Study of Drug Dependence (ISDD), 32-36 Loman Street, London SE1 0EE. The series includes booklets on heroin, LSD, cannabis, amphetamines, cocaine and crack, solvents, tranquillisers, ecstasy, anabolic steroids, over-the-counter medicines and 'poppers'. Each consists of a description of the drug, the history of its use, the law, its prevalence and availability, short-term effects and long-term consequences. Other topics are covered in addition in some booklets, such as issues in the response to heroin misuse in Britain, production and trafficking in the cannabis booklet, what substances are sniffed and responses to volatile substance abuse (VSA) in Britain, medical use and issues in benzodiazepine use. The over-the-counter medicines booklet is divided into medicines with opiate-like effects, medicines with sedative-like effects and medicines with stimulant-like effects.

The ISDD also produces a series of five small leaflets entitled Drug Information for Women:

- Drugs and their effects
- Drugs and your health
- Drugs and pregnancy
- Drugs and your rights
- Going to a drug agency.

References

1 Morrison, C., Siney, C. (1995). 'Maternity services for drug misusers in England and Wales: a national survey', Health Trends, Vol. 27, No.1.

2 Rooney, C. (Ed.) (1992). Antenatal Care and Maternal Health: How Effective is it? A Review of the Evidence. Geneva: WHO.

3 Kline, J., Stein, Z., Hutzler, M. (1987). 'Cigarettes, alcohol and marijuana: varying associations with birthweight', International Journal of Epidemiology, Vol. 16, pp.44-51.

4 Siney, C., Kidd, M., Walkinshaw, S., Morrison, C., Manasse, P. (1995). 'Opiate dependency in pregnancy', British Journal of Midwifery, February, Vol. 3, No. 2, pp.69-73.

5 Connaughton, J.F., Reeser, D.S. (1977). 'Management of the pregnant opiate addict: success with a comprehensive approach', American Journal of Obstetrics and Gynaecology, Vol. 129 (678), pp.7-8.

6 UKCC (1992). Code of Professional Conduct.

7 The Children Act (1989).

8 Advisory Council on the Misuse of Drugs (1993). AIDS and Drug Misuse Update. London: HMSO.

9 Morrison, C., Siney, C. (1996). 'A survey of the management of neonatal opiate withdrawal', European Journal of Paediatrics, 155, pp323-326.

10 Tanne, H.J. (1992). 'Forcing treatment on pregnant women', British Medical Journal, Vol. 305, No. 6845, pp.76-77.

11 Tanne, H.J. (1991). 'Jail for pregnant cocaine users in the United States', British Medical Journal, Vol. 303, No. 6807, p.873.

Sources

Parker, H., Bakx, K., Newcombe, R. (1986). 'Drug misuse in Wirral: a study of eighteen hundred problem drug users known to official agencies'. The First Report of the Wirral Misuse of Drugs Project, University of Liverpool.

Pearson, G. (1987). 'Social deprivation, unemployment and patterns of heroin use'. In: Dorn, N., South, N (Eds). A Land Fit for Heroin? Drug Policies, Prevention and Practice. London: Macmillan.

Pearson, G. (1991). 'Drug-control policies in Britain'. In: Tonry, M. Crime and Justice. Chicago: University of Chicago Press.

Social Services Inspectorate (1991). 'Community based services for people who misuse drugs: a study in North Western Region'. London: Department of Health.

Chapter 2

MANAGEMENT OF PREGNANT WOMEN WHO ARE DRUG-DEPENDENT

INCLUDING THE LIVERPOOL MODEL

Catherine Siney

Catherine Siney is the specialist midwife liaison at the Liverpool Women's Hospital. She coordinates the obstetric and gynaecology services for women who are drug and/or alcohol dependent or who are HIV or hepatitis positive. She began the service in 1990 and is responsible for the training of all staff around the issues of drugs, HIV and hepatitis. In 1993 the service was cited as an example of good practice in 'The A-Z of Quality' NHS Executive. She was the midwife member of the working groups who assisted the ENB to develop 'Substance use and misuse: guidelines for good practice in training of nurses, midwives and health visitors' in 1996. She has published many papers and articles in national and international journals and regularly speaks at conferences and seminars at home and abroad.

Pregnancy outcomes in drug-dependent women have been reported for 20 years or more. The pregnancies of these women have always been regarded as 'high risk', both obstetrically and paediatrically. However, it should be remembered that the majority, and the earliest, of these outcome papers are from America, and in America the least advantaged and the most needy people, have the least access to healthcare. The links between infant/maternal mortality and poverty, poor health and nutrition are well documented and all the problems associated with drug misuse and dependence are also associated with social deprivation. There are many medical problems associated with heavy drug use, including anaemia and chronic bronchitis, and these and others are fully covered in the chapter on medical problems; other chapters cover human immunodeficiency virus (HIV), hepatitis and sexually transmitted infections.

In general, the main problems for the babies are intrauterine growth retardation, the risk of prematurity and, if the mother is opiate dependent, neonatal withdrawal problems. However, acute withdrawal of opiates during pregnancy may precipitate enough distress in the fetus for spontaneous abortion or intrauterine death to occur. Indeed there are risks to the wellbeing of both mother and fetus of acute withdrawal from not only opiates but also barbiturates and benzodiazepenes. It is, therefore, essential that any antenatal care offered allows the woman to reduce these drugs of dependence slowly. Other drugs may usually just be stopped; maintenance of stimulant drugs, for example cocaine or tobacco, is inappropriate.

Management of pregnancy in women who are drug dependent must be holistic – this means not seeing these women as a collection of problems but as women whose pregnancies are just part of a larger picture of their lives. Over the years great store has been set in pregnancy acting as a catalyst for women to stop misusing drugs, but in our experience at the Liverpool Women's Hospital this has not usually proved to be the case. In many instances, however, the lifestyles of women who were chaotic have become less so and many women already within a treatment programme have reduced their methadone or reduced/stopped using illicit drugs during their pregnancies. Some women have even managed to reduce their tobacco smoking. I think it is important that professionals involved with the pregnant woman should remember that, although all information about possible risks to the baby should be given, she should be supported in whatever attempts she makes to improve her health, and information should be given, and questions answered, in a non-judgmental way.

There have been programmes of maternity care involving a multidisciplinary approach since the 1970s in America and since the 1980s in the United Kingdom. In the early 1970s a programme was started in New York State which aimed to stabilise the women's life situations by offering a methadone programme and assistance to secure financial, legal and housing services. At the end of the first year 104 women had been referred to the programme and the conclusion drawn then was that a methadone programme, together with a great deal of psycho-social support, alleviated many of the common problems associated with drug dependence and pregnancy.[1]

In the 1980s Fraser[2] published a report on 72 pregnancies that had occurred between 1967 and 1982, describing their outcomes. The report concluded that management was complex, with medical and social problems both during the pregnancy and afterward, and recommended an early case conference. Strang and Moran,[3] working in Manchester at the Regional Drug Dependence Unit, stressed the importance of combining antenatal care with a drug reduction programme and said that parenting skills should be judged by the same criteria applied to non drug-dependent women. Dixon's article in Druglink[4] gave a comprehensive view of the management of pregnant drug-dependent women from a social work perspective and concluded that each family situation should be looked at individually.

The 1990s have shown larger numbers of drug-dependent women having babies and much work, including papers by Dawe, Gerada and Strang,[5] Fraser and Cavanagh[6] and Hepburn,[7] has talked of the importance of liaison and outreach services for female drug users.

Pre-conception care

General education about contraception to prevent unwanted pregnancy should be given to all women who enter treatment services or who have contact with outreach services (see Chapter 9, 'The Sexual Health Needs of Female Drug Users' and Chapter 11, 'Outreach Work with Female Sex Workers in Liverpool'). If pregnancy is planned then general health needs should be addressed, including rubella antibody screening, and any chronic medical problems should be discussed, including the effects on pregnancy and the fetus. For example, opiate-dependent women with epilepsy may have no idea about their epileptic condition and the taking of anticonvulsants in pregnancy. The benefits of regular eating habits, a reduction in tobacco smoking and discussion about increased problems with constipation is useful. (Regular opiate use, including methadone, may affect bowel habits.)

Late booking

There are many reasons for late booking for hospital delivery. The problem of women not realising they are pregnant until fetal movement is felt, or until other physical changes occur, can be addressed by early contraceptive advice and access to pregnancy testing. For women who have no general practitioner (GP), the medical staff at the drug agencies should be able to refer pregnant women direct to an obstetrician, together with a letter with relevant drug history information, including any history of intravenous injecting. Women who are not in contact with drug agencies should be able to contact a specialist midwife at the maternity unit to access maternity care. In Liverpool, information about the specialist midwife and the named consultants is distributed by means of a poster with a covering letter, to GPs and to other relevant areas and departments by the Family Health Services Authority (FHSA).

The Liverpool Model

Although pregnancies complicated by drug use and/or dependency are generally considered to be obstetrically 'high risk', it is often difficult to give these women care at all. The Liverpool Women's Hospital has tried to operate a system of normalisation for them; we therefore decided that as long as the women were given antenatal care monthly by someone it did not really matter whether this was hospital care, by an obstetrician, or community care by a midwife or GP. The result has been that the women have accepted that monthly attendance somewhere for antenatal care is the minimum required to monitor the wellbeing of both themselves and their babies. Once women are known to the specialist midwife, a bed booking is confirmed at the hospital. This means that even if the women do not attend the hospital until they are in labour, or until they experience an antenatal problem, basic health, drug and social information is available, together with notes on any follow-up antenatal visits by the specialist midwife, in the hospital records for the hospital staff.

Parent education

Parent education is offered to all women attending the hospital in the form of classes at different times of the day, including evenings; however it is also available on a one-to-one basis, and for those women who are unable or do not wish to attend in the antenatal period then the parent education midwife can visit the women on the ward in the postnatal period. The general education includes information about the types of analgesia available in labour, an insight into the 24-hour responsibility of parenting and basic instruction in bathing and infant feeding.

Screening and scans

An ultrasound scan for fetal anomalies is offered at 18 to 20 weeks, (or at the first opportunity if the women enter the service after that), and at 28 weeks and 34 weeks' gestation. We thought at one time that ultrasound scans would attract the women to attend hospital more often but found that, although it worked occasionally to encourage the women to attend for the first scan, sometimes they would attend for ultrasound and then not carry on to the antenatal clinic appointment which followed. For those women not in touch with formal services, the first ultrasound scan is usually arranged by the specialist midwife at the time she meets the women, by telephone if one is available, and women are told that they can just turn up but will probably have to wait to be fitted in. However, whenever possible, if the women can give a time and day that will suit them then formal appointments are made.

Routine blood tests for blood grouping and antibodies, a full blood count and rubella antibodies are offered, but we also offer testing for hepatitis B surface antigen and antibodies, and in 1994 we added testing for hepatitis C for women with a past or current history of intravenous drug use. (Hepatitis B vaccination for the newborn baby is advised routinely if the women are hepatitis B surface antigen positive during pregnancy.) Although HIV is discussed, women are usually asked to discuss this further with their drug agency, if they have one, or with the local Genito-Urinary Medicine department where long-term support facilities are available. Since the specialist midwife is available at the drug clinic/GP surgeries, on either a regular or an ad hoc basis, HIV testing is discussed jointly on most occasions. Details of previous HIV tests are recorded in the hospital records only if the women wish it. A combined blood test to ascertain the level of risk of Down's Syndrome and open neural tube defects is offered to women if they attend early enough in their pregnancies, that is between 15 and 20 weeks' gestation. A specimen of urine is sent for screening for infection and care is taken to reassure the women that urine is never screened for drugs without their express permission.

Antenatal care

The antenatal care given by the specialist midwife, hospital obstetrician or GP surgery is the same care given to any pregnant woman. However, eating, tobacco smoking and alcohol habits are discussed in detail because regular drug use may depress appetite and tobacco use may be much heavier in drug-dependent women; advice is also given about constipation. If women are prescribed injectable methadone or continue to inject illicit drugs during pregnancy it is important to know that they are using safe injection techniques and clean equipment. Women who usually inject into their groin may have problems as their stomachs enlarge; therefore, if they have no partner to inject for them, an alternative site needs to be suggested. Ideally, of course, injecting anything, whether prescribed or illicit, should be discouraged. We have had occasional problems with women injecting into breast veins and this can cause problems of mastitis and necrosis. Injectable methadone is not prescribed during hospital admissions.

Drug treatment regime

The treatment regime for pregnant opiate-dependent women by the local drug clinic – the Liverpool Drug Dependency Unit (LDDU) – is one of stabilisation of opiate dependency on to an amount of daily methadone (either oral or for injecting, depending on what is appropriate for the woman) in the first trimester. Reduction in the community is by a maximum of 5mgs per week at any one time after the first trimester and this can continue throughout pregnancy if the women wish it. With women who are new into the local drug clinic as pregnant priority clients, the aim will be to stabilise drug use, and these women will be encouraged to reduce their prescription during pregnancy. Clients already involved with the drug clinic may reduce their prescriptions if they are stable. However for some women, who come late in pregnancy into treatment, the main aim will be to stabilise them. Some women will be able to reduce their prescription throughout the whole pregnancy and some women may have to have a small increase towards the end of the pregnancy. The women are always told of the theoretical risks associated with suddenly stopping opiates and of the risks of stopping barbiturates and benzodiazepines. If they want to stop we offer them either an in-patient maternity bed, or daily access to the fetal wellbeing unit, where the wellbeing of the fetus can be monitored, or they may be offered a bed in the drug detoxification unit, whichever is most appropriate. The LDDU works within a harm minimisation framework, negotiating individual treatment plans with their service users.

Women are always assured that methadone will be available to them, whether in a treatment programme or not, for any admission to hospital.

Women are always encouraged to reduce their overall drug use (prescribed and illicit) during the pregnancy, which includes their use of tobacco and alcohol.

Social issues

It is essential for all professionals in contact with pregnant women who are drug dependent to be sure that these women will be able to care adequately for their children when they go home from hospital. Because of the system of normalisation within our hospital, the hospital social services department, the paediatric liaison health visitor and the specialist midwife meet each month, or more often, to discuss all the drug-dependent women known to the maternity service. Information is gathered from all professionals in contact with the women and the need for formal input or a child protection conference is decided from this information. (The LDDU also have a regular meeting to discuss their pregnant clients and the social workers at the LDDU make any assessment needed.)

If a child protection conference is required then this is usually arranged at least six weeks before the expected date of confinement. Having child protection conferences in advance of the delivery allows plans to be made and accepted and this in turn means that when the women deliver their babies the plans for child care are available to hospital staff in the hospital records. This enables the women and their babies to be discharged when obstetrically/paediatrically fit. Women and hospital staff generally have a happier time if everyone knows the plan and the hospital staff are able to reinforce the need for the women to comply with any agreed plan for child care.

Care in labour

All types of analgesia are available to the women in labour unless there is a medical contra-indication, for example, in the case of epidural analgesia the women must fulfil the safety criteria of the anaesthetist. Analgesia is given alongside the prescribed methadone – if a woman is not registered for treatment then the level of methadone needed to maintain the woman's comfort is assessed and given. We have found that opiate-dependent women who have their methadone level maintained do not require any more analgesia in labour, or post-operatively, than other women.

Methadone is prescribed for the women as a daily dose so that they can ask for their medication at the usual time they take it and they can split up their medication as they would at home; also they may not actually require the full amount prescribed. The local drug prescribing agencies are well aware that their clients may vary their methadone dose. Injectable methadone is not available for in-patients in the hospital; this policy was agreed by the consultant in drug dependency at the LDDU, the obstetricians and the senior hospital pharmacist. During labour the fetus is monitored continually using a cardiotocograph. A paediatrician may be present for the delivery. Many of the babies have proved to be growth retarded at birth and if so, specific instructions regarding feeding may be required.

The use of naloxone hydrochloride for neonates by midwives (to reverse opioid-induced respiratory depression) has been discontinued in our hospital following an audit by a paediatric consultant of the use of this drug in the delivery suite (see Chapter 6, 'Maternal drug use: consequences for the child'). It was felt that any benefit that there might be was outweighed by the risk that it might be given to the baby of an unknown opiate-dependent woman, precipitating an acute opiate withdrawal crisis. This is a cause for concern as drug misuse in Liverpool is a large and growing problem and it seemed prudent to acknowledge this. Adult naloxone hydrochloride is available to the paediatrician for use for resuscitation purposes.

Post-delivery care

Mothers and babies are cared for together within the postnatal area. Admission to the neonatal intensive care unit is for medical reasons only and not for observation. Babies are monitored four-hourly using the drug withdrawal chart. Symptoms and the minimum length of time required for a postnatal stay are discussed at length during the antenatal period, and again after the birth. Most women are distressed to see their babies suffering the effects of drug withdrawal and many are surprised when the degree is different from that they have been led to expect from other women. We try not to make the women feel any more guilty than they do already, and give as much support as the women need to care for babies who may be difficult to settle. If treatment is required, the babies stay with the mothers and the paediatricians and midwives spend time explaining what is happening and why the baby needs treatment. We try very hard not to make it seem like a punishment for their drug use. By treating neonatal opiate withdrawal as a paediatric medical problem and not as a moral issue we have found that women are anxious for their babies to receive whatever treatment they require, and for as long as necessary. It is very unusual for women to go home and leave their babies in hospital, unless a long stay in the neonatal unit is required. The urine or meconium of babies of drug dependent women is not sent for drug screening; neither are the babies HIV tested. Any baby whose mother is found to be hepatitis B surface antigen positive during pregnancy or labour is offered prophylactic hepatitis B vaccination. We are constantly reviewing our care of the babies of drug-dependent women and have altered the neonatal drug withdrawal chart since the specialist service began in 1990. The use of charts is discussed in Chapter 1, in the section 'Effects of drugs on pregnancy and the neonate'.

Breastfeeding is encouraged if the woman is stable on a methadone programme. However, many of the women we care for are polydrug users of both prescribed and illicit drugs and we do not encourage these women to breastfeed since we cannot assure them of the safety of their babies. Only a very small number of women have actually wanted to breastfeed their babies; one woman has breastfed both her children and despite the fact that she was on prescriptions of more than 30 milligrams of methadone daily, neither of the babies required any treatment for opiate withdrawal syndrome.

The midwives working in the community are notified when drug-dependent women and their babies are discharged from hospital, so that they can give them the support and reassurance that they need. Babies are never discharged from hospital until any treatment has been completed. If babies show either no signs of withdrawal, or only mild signs, after 72 hours then they are discharged home soon afterwards, once the mothers are happy that they can cope with the babies' needs.

The health visitors are notified antenatally by the paediatric liaison health visitor so that if the women are unknown to them they can visit and establish contact before birth.

Future contraceptive needs are discussed during the antenatal period, in hospital and by the community staff, and if female sterilisation is an option then an appointment is made for a later date to discuss this.

Aims of the specialist service

The aims of the service have been to normalise the care of pregnant drug-dependent women, and to create an attractive, easily accessible service that gives them a positive birth experience. The service has proved to be accessible, with increased numbers of women approaching either before their pregnancies or earlier in their pregnancies, and it has also reduced the ratio of drug-dependent women arriving unbooked and in labour.

We feel in Liverpool that it is important to try to assess the motivation of the pregnant woman and her plans for her drug use. It is important to have realistic expectations about the drug use from both the woman and the health care professionals. Professionals must remember that although it would be good to have a drug-free mother at delivery this must not be at the risk of destabilising a lifestyle that enables her to care for her new baby and/or any other children.

Training for staff

The specialist midwife organises study days to discuss drugs and pregnancy and associated issues for all grades of staff. It is hoped that staff will not only gain information from these sessions but will also look at their attitudes so that they can ensure that all women in their care receive the care they are entitled to without fear of bias. The hospital is constantly reviewing clinical practice to ensure the safety of all patients and staff.

The Liverpool model has been very effective for managing the obstetric and gynaecological needs of women who are drug and/or alcohol dependent when there are very large numbers, and the role of a drug liaison midwife is very useful when working with many different drug agencies and general practitioners.

However, if there are only small numbers of drug-dependent women then the model would need to be adapted to suit particular circumstances. For example, a small maternity unit might need to have an access point – a telephone answering machine which can be cleared by a midwife who works flexibly, increasing or decreasing the amount of time she needs dependent on the numbers.

There must be clear lines of communication between all agencies, whether statutory or voluntary, together with a good understanding of what each agency actually does, and a respect for the opinions of all the professionals who may have care of or responsibility for the drug-dependent woman. This ensures that everyone concerned, including the woman, knows what is being said at all times, and that she and her family have as good an experience as possible.

References

1 Harper, R.G., Solish, G.I., Purow, H.M., Sang, E., Panepinto, W.C. (1974). 'The effect of a methadone treatment programme upon heroin addicts and their newborn infants', Paediatrics, Vol. 54, No. 3 September, pp.300-305.

2 Fraser, A.C. (1983). 'The pregnant drug addict', Maternal and Child Health, November, pp.461-63.

3 Strang, J., Moran, C. (1985). 'The pregnant drug addict'. Manchester (unpublished).

4 Dixon, A. (1987). 'The pregnant addict', Druglink, July/August, pp.6-8.

5 Dawe, S., Gerada, C., Strang, J. (1992). 'Establishment of a liaison service for pregnant opiate dependent women', British Journal of Addiction, Vol. 87, No. 6 June, pp.867-71.

6 Fraser, A.C., Cavanagh, S. (1991). 'Pregnancy and drug addiction - long term consequences', Journal of Royal Society of Medicine, Vol. 84, September, pp.530-32.

7 Hepburn, M. (1993). 'Drug use in pregnancy', British Journal of Hospital Medicine, Vol. 49, No. 1, pp.51-55.

Chapter 3

WOMEN & DRUG USE

Sue Ruben

Dr Susan M. Ruben is Consultant Psychiatrist at the Liverpool Drug Dependency Clinic. She qualified at Edinburgh University in 1978. Dr Ruben is a Fellow of the Royal College of Psychiatrists. She has specialised in drug misuse for the last ten years and is on the Executive Committee of the Substance Misuse Section of the College and a member of the Advisory Council on the Misuse of Drugs. In 1994 Dr Ruben was Liverpool Echo's 'Mum of the Year'.

Illegal drug use has increased markedly all over the world. Treatment agencies are generally preoccupied with treating male drug misusers. However, although the overall number of women is lower than men, there is considerable evidence to suggest that the number of women using and experiencing severe problems with illegal drugs is increasing.

Women are often reluctant to take advantage of treatments that are available to them. The social stigma around drug use is probably worse for women than men as it very much goes against their perceived role as carers and the perception that they should in some way be more responsible than men. In common with alcohol use in women, drug taking is often hidden. Women experience extreme guilt, and fear that admitting the problem will have worse consequences, with particular regard to their children, than trying to cope without expert help. Professionals therefore need to take seriously the particular issues for women and to try to ensure that services for drug users take account of women's needs and fears, working with their women users to overcome prejudice.

Why do women misuse drugs?

Women who become problematic drug users may do so for a huge variety of reasons. They are often introduced to drugs by drug-taking sexual partners (who may see no problem in their own drug use but may be extremely critical of the woman when she follows their lead).

Drug taking may be used to alleviate stress, anxiety and depression or may be entered into initially as a recreational activity without recognising the serious consequences that may ensue. In my experience women's veins do not seem to withstand injecting for as long as men's veins, and women often run into early problems with injection sites.

Women with children are in constant fear that if they admit their problem, their children will be taken into care by social workers. It is therefore imperative that drug services look to reducing this as a consequence and work closely with local social services departments to ensure that systems can be put in place which reduce this possibility.

Clearly there cannot be a blanket statement that no woman drug user will have their child removed, as under the Children's Act the care of the child and its needs are paramount. However, statements that drug use per se is not a reason for removing children, and that every opportunity will be used to try and keep children with their drug-using mothers, can realistically help in reassuring women. One would hope that, in good treatment facilities, women who accept their problems and work towards solving them in a positive way would be less likely to experience child-care problems than those who are not in touch with treatment, and this needs to be constantly striven for.

Services need to be aware of the ways in which women obtain money to sustain a drug habit. Prostitution has increasingly become a mode of obtaining money to buy drugs and this in itself causes major problems for women. Firstly, prostitution is an extremely risky profession. The woman is at risk from a health point of view with regard to sexually transmitted infections, HIV and hepatitis B (these will be dealt with in other chapters). They are also at risk of physical abuse by their clients. The work is often done in unsafe places such as red light districts in cities and, in order to overcome their distaste for prostitution, many women find that their drug use escalates out of control. This can lead to a rapid down-spiralling in terms of their abilities to cope and survive. While it is relatively easy to earn money as a prostitute, if the drug use escalates this clearly does not help the individual to survive in a safe way within our modern society.

Once women enter into the criminal justice system, this again tends to have very serious negative effects with regard to their family relationships and care for their children. Whereas men going to prison, for example, can usually rely on women left outside to continue with parental roles and child rearing, this is often not an option for women and imprisonment is extremely disruptive to any possibility of them parenting their children successfully.

Treatment

Treatment of women drug users, in my view, requires a multidisciplinary approach with a range of input from interested professionals. Often, in addition to problems with drug use in their lives, they have a multitude of social, emotional and financial difficulties with associated chronic low self-esteem. All these aspects of their lives need to be tackled if they are either to overcome their drug problems or benefit from substitution treatments such as methadone. Interventions need to take account of the individual's particular needs and deficits and aim to work with the woman in a positive way. Health care professionals should always emphasise what can be done and how women can take control of their lives again, while recognising that helping any individual with a drug problem can be a time-consuming business. The natural history of serious drug misuse is that it is a recurring condition with periods of relative stability; it is easy to fall back into more problematic use with its attendant consequences.

This again puts women under particular pressures and, during periods of chaos, their social problems and inability to care adequately for their children may cause yet more stress and difficulties for them.

The first thing treatment agencies must do is to ensure that women have ready access into treatment. This can be relatively successfully helped by, for example, the use of specific outreach workers with female drug users, in particular with female prostitutes. They can be the important first link for a woman into the helping system. As well as giving high quality advice on the spread of sexually transmitted infections, HIV and hepatitis, they can encourage women to take up a treatment option and, if need be, accompany them to an appointment. Treatment agencies need to educate social services and primary health care teams in considering drug misuse in women who are having particular problems in coping.

Treatment agencies can ensure that their facility is welcoming for women by having an area with toys for children to play with, baby changing facilities and leaflets that particularly emphasise women's issues, to ensure that women do not feel ostracised or criticised by seeking help. Agencies should constantly be monitoring their referral patterns to ensure that women are being referred and, if not, they should take active steps to encourage referrals.

It is worth having particular staff members take a clear interest in women and their particular problems, and introducing women drug users to them early on in treatment. We have found in Liverpool that the policy of prioritising female prostitutes and pregnant users into the methadone programme has been very helpful in encouraging women to come forward for help and treatment.

In my experience the treatment options which might be offered to a woman are no different than those that could be offered to any drug user regardless of sex. However particular attention may be needed to ensure that women can take advantage of treatment facilities and are able to keep regular appointments with the drug clinic team. It is pointless giving women with children appointments which clash with school times and it may be more appropriate to try to offer a lot of the support in the person's own home, if this can be arranged and the woman is agreeable.

The philosophy of harm minimisation

It is my belief that the sort of interventions that are available for drug users should fall broadly within a philosophy of harm minimisation. By that, I mean that all interventions offered to people should have an objective of reducing the harm that their drug-taking behaviour is causing both to them as individuals and also to their family and the community as a whole.

The overall aim of any harm minimisation programme should be ultimately for people to lead a drug-free life and to be self-supporting in their community. It also has to be recognised that this is often an unrealistic initial goal for people and intermediate goals are worth setting on the way to a drug-free life. We must acknowledge that not all individuals are going to achieve the ultimate goal but if they manage improvements in their social stability, general health, injecting behaviour and ability to care for their children, this in itself is positive and worth achieving.

Consideration has to be given, of course, to the treatment options depending on the drug or drugs used by women. In general, women's drug use reflects the pattern of drug use in the community in which they live. Currently, in the UK it is still true to say that the most common problematic illegal drug is heroin. However drugs such as the stimulants cocaine and amphetamines are commonly used, and minor tranquilizers, particularly benzodiazepines, are commonly misused. The dangers of the abuse of sleeping preparations such as temazepam cannot be over-emphasised. It is also well known that women are more likely to be prescribed benzodiazepine than men and therefore benzodiazepine abuse is extremely common in this group.

Many women are 'polydrug abusers' – they use and abuse more than one class of drug. All this has to be taken into account in the initial assessment period. At the first assessment a decision needs to be made as to whether any form of prescription is likely to be helpful or whether the individual should be helped by counselling, support or other forms of intervention, such as a rapid detoxification programme.

Oral methadone

Experience has shown that people who are highly dependent on opiate-class drugs tend to benefit from a period of stabilisation on an opiate substitute. In the UK, the most commonly prescribed drug for this purpose is oral methadone. Oral methadone has major advantages; firstly it is well absorbed orally and has been shown consistently to reduce injecting behaviours. Secondly, it is a long-acting drug and it can therefore be taken on a once-daily or twice-daily basis. This stabilises the individual's mental state and can enable them, with assistance, to start planning and organising their life in a more appropriate and positive manner. It has to be recognised that methadone is itself an opiate drug and therefore highly addictive. It therefore does not cure addiction but can enable an unstable addict to become a stable addict with a legal prescription and with no drug-related need to resort to criminal activity. It also enables the person to work on other aspects of their life.

Many women have poor coping skills and strategies and need considerable assistance with things such as managing money, caring for children, health care and developing social skills. My experience is that the input of people such as specialist health visitors and social workers can be invaluable in assisting the woman to organise herself and her family more successfully while she is on a prescription.

During treatment with methadone, urine testing can form part of a vital strategy for monitoring the individual's drug use on top of their prescription. It gives workers a way of monitoring progress and it can, if used properly, help the drug user to stabilise their own life. Usually, on methadone programmes the use of other drugs on top of the prescription significantly reduces and around 50 per cent of people can be expected over time to stop altogether. While it is clearly desirable that, wherever possible, methadone prescription should be for as short a time as possible, experience has shown that for some individuals who are attempting to stabilise other aspects of their life, the prescription may be for a longer time than would have initially been desirable. This should not be seen as failure but rather as an inevitable consequence of trying to help individuals with very many social and other problems.

The most important thing in a successful methadone programme appears to be a good working relationship between the drug user and the staff on that programme. It is essential to encourage people to be honest and open with the staff while reassuring them that they will not be punished for honesty.

In-patient detoxification

For other female drug users it may be more appropriate to consider a period of in-patient detoxification. The team must ensure that adequate provision has been made for any children of the woman, so that while she is in hospital the children are well cared for. Strenuous efforts have to be made to ensure that the children can visit their mother whilst she is in hospital and that the children themselves have appropriate support so that they can cope without their mother. They may be very anxious about their mother, particularly if they have been aware that she has not been well and have not been aware of the reason for her behaviour towards them.

Once successfully detoxified, it is absolutely vital that appropriate aftercare is organised for the woman and her family. This may take the form of opiate-antagonist drugs such as naltrexone. Appropriate support/counselling and training opportunities also seem to be vital during this time.

For a small proportion of women, longer-term rehabilitation in family units away from their usual community may be required. There are very few such units in the UK. Costs often prove prohibitive, as these currently have to be met by overstretched social services monies for care in the community, and some programmes last for up to 12 months.

I have tried therefore to emphasise the positive gains that can be offered to women drug users, their particular difficulties and some general ways in which the needs of women as service users must be addressed. Individuals working with women drug users need to examine their own attitudes and take into account the fact that these may adversely affect a woman in treatment, and all multidisciplinary teams need to constantly review and reassess the particular needs of their women drug users as they arise.

Sources

Ashton, H., Golding, J.F. (1989). 'Tranquilizers: prevalence, predictors and possible consequences. Data from a large UK survey', British Journal of Addiction, Vol. 84, pp.541-46.

Martin, C.A., Marin, W.R. (1980). 'Opiate Dependence in Women.' In: Kalant, O.J. (Ed.) Alcohol and Drug Problems in Women. New York: Plenum.

Medical Working Group on Drug Dependence (1992). 'Guidelines of good clinical practices for the treatment of drug misuse'. London: DHSS.

Rosenbaum, M. (1981). Women on Heroin. New Jersey: Rutgers University Press.

Chapter 4

THE MEDICAL PROBLEMS OF ILLICIT DRUG USE IN PREGNANCY & HARM MINIMIZATION

Clive L. Morrison

Dr Clive L. Morrison is a vocational trained General Practitioner and has worked for four years in substance misuse and HIV prevention. In his role as Senior Clinical Medical Officer for Special Groups he provides family health care for drug users, prostitutes and HIV positive people. He has a unique expertise in the management of the complications of injecting drug misuse.

He has a special interest in the care and prescribing of methadone to pregnant drug users within the Liverpool Drug Dependency Clinic. Another role is to liaise between the local GUM and Drug Dependency services. He has collaborated in many research projects with allied health professionals, including the Regional Infectious Diseases Unit, with a particular emphasis on the health care needs of drug users.

The misuse of drugs, particularly the injecting misuse, carries with it considerable mortality and morbidity. Users often hide their problems for fear of being discovered as an addict. Judgmental attitudes towards drug users from health care staff can also prevent users gaining access to the normal emergency medical services via casualty or general practice. This tends to exacerbate problems which could have been easily resolved with simple treatments if presented earlier. The user appears to have neglected her condition. In reality it is the health services that have excluded her from care.

The problems of drug misuse affect men and women equally, but when a woman is pregnant issues become more emotive. Rather than being seen as an individual, with the right to lead her own lifestyle, she is treated more as a 'baby machine' with problems which are considered to be both self-inflicted and harmful to her pregnancy. These effects are largely related to the illegal nature of drugs and to having no access to needle and syringe exchanges. Having clean needles and syringes and receiving safer drug-use advice from drug agencies within a harm minimisation framework reduces the problems of drug misuse. However, misusers can still encounter accidental overdosage, withdrawal symptoms, cardiac and pulmonary problems, dental caries, abscesses, cellulitis, endocarditis, septicaemia, viral hepatitis, genito-urinary infections and HIV (some of these aspects are covered in other chapters).

Overdosage and withdrawal

One of the problems of illicit drug use is that users obtain irregular supplies from the illegal market. Concentrations of the drug can vary, even from the supplier, depending upon how much the drug is adulterated. The higher the profit motive, the more the drug will be diluted along the chain of supply. If a woman has become accustomed to injecting a certain supply which then becomes more concentrated, then there is a potential to overdose.

Opiate overdose requires immediate hospitalisation to monitor any respiratory suppression and also to prevent asphyxiation after vomiting.

The opiate antagonist, naloxone usually brings a quick recovery. Pulmonary oedema is one of the most common and serious effects of heroin overdose. Some far-sighted agencies instruct users in life support techniques that could be used whilst waiting for an ambulance if an acquaintance succumbs to overdosage. Radical proposals have suggested that drug users should be issued with naloxone ampoules that they could inject as required. However, it is believed that naloxone would be too dangerous to use outside hospital, and pregnant women would certainly need adequate fetal monitoring.

The misuse of tricyclic anti-depressants, cocaine and cyclizine can cause cardiac arrythmias and, when this causes sudden death, it is usually considered as an overdose. It has been estimated that around one per cent of injecting drug users die this way each year. At the other end of the spectrum is withdrawal, which in pregnancy can cause miscarriage in the first trimester, fetal compromise and premature labour in the final trimester.

The symptoms of opiate withdrawal in the adult include rhinorrhoea, lachrymation, abdominal cramps, gooseflesh, diarrhoea, muscle cramps and insomnia. Opiates are the only illicit drugs that cause a physical dependence and there is no adult morbidity associated with opiate withdrawal. Opiate withdrawal can be managed easily by using the oral substitute methadone. The amount used can be titrated according to the suggested table below.

Methadone equivalents for drug of dependence

Drug	Dose	Methadone equivalent
Street Heroin	1/4 g	20 mg*
Pharmaceutical Heroin	30 mg ampoule	50 mg
Dipipanone	10 mg	4 mg
Codeine Phosphate	30 mg	2 mg
Dihydrocodeine	30 mg	3 mg
Dextromoramide	10 mg	10-20 mg
Buprenorphine	200 mcg	5 mg
Codeine Linctus	100 ml	10 mg

* Dose varies according to purity available in the community. Drug services will have the appropriate experience to titrate according to the local illicit supply.

In areas where there are well-developed drug treatment agencies, the obstetric services should not involve themselves with the intricacies of methadone prescribing and should seek at all times the advice of their health care colleagues, hopefully within the structure of an obstetric liaison service.

The other illicit drugs such as cocaine, amphetamines or LSD do not create any physical dependence. The psychological dependency to these drugs can be considerable but there are no physical symptoms associated with abrupt withdrawal, or any evidence of harm to the fetus.

Dental hygiene

In any group of observed drug misusers on methadone there is a high rate of dental caries. Generally users have poor individual dental hygiene care and blame the high sugar content of methadone mixture, but there has been no research to make any conclusions on this. Users have difficulty in accessing dental care due to dentists' fears of cross infection, but the level of anxiety related to dental treatment is still as high as the general population, even though drug misusers may be injectors themselves. As a consequence of multiple dental caries, dental abscesses are common. A thorough dental assessment with appropriate referral should be performed at the appointment for booking antenatal care. Poor dental hygiene allows for the copious growth of anaerobes in oral secretions and these are commonly involved in aspiration pneumonia. Symptoms may be only minor and present for many weeks. Eventually lung abscesses may form but these may not show on X-ray until a cavity lesion is present.

Respiratory system problems

Pulmonary vascular granulomatosis can occur in injecting drug users when they inject crushed tablets (such as dipipanone and methadone) that are intended for oral use. The granulomas are an immune reaction to the talc that is used in tablets to bulk and carry the active drug. The illness presents as progressively increasing shortness of breath in association with a productive cough. These symptoms can also occur in heroin use, when the adulterants in the drug can embolise to the lung, including fibres from cigarette filters, which are commonly used by drug users to filter out residue when preparing heroin to inject.

Pieces of needles being used to inject drugs can break off, particularly in very fibrous injecting sites and embolise to the lung but these are best treated consecutively.

Research in the United States suggests that the incidence of tubercular disease in drug users is higher than in the general population due to factors related to lifestyle such as poor nutrition, close contact and depressed state of health due to other infections. In New York 20 per cent of drug users had positive screening tests for TB. Some drug treatment agencies have added prophylactic anti-tubercular chemotherapy into the oral methadone for such drug users. However, in the UK public health and social policies are completely different, with the school BCG vaccination programme and welfare limiting poverty to some extent. There is no such association with drug users and TB in this country other than for social class.

Inhaling the fumes of heroin can also be problematic. The drug releases histamine and this process can produce asthma. The snorting of cocaine can damage the cartilage between the nostrils and produce a perforation. Snorting any drug can increase the incidence of rhinorrhoea, allergic rhinitis and infected sinuses.

Injecting drug users are more likely to acquire chest infections than the general population. The risk is ten times greater but the infection responds well to the usual treatments. Pulmonary fungal infection has occurred, the cause being identified as due to the presence of candida albicans in lemon juice. This is used to acidify and to help the solution to dissolve illicit heroin, to render it injectable.

Subcutaneous, deep, mycotic and septicaemic infections

Local skin infections are the most common presentation in injecting drug misusers. This clinical problem ranges from small abscesses, cellulitis, thrombophlebitis to necrotising fascitis. The predominant organisms isolated from such infections are usually staphylococci and streptococci. Infections that remain localised without systemic effects can be treated with either magnesium sulphate dressings at an early stage or, if the abscess is pointing, incised and drained. The antibiotic of choice is either flucloxacillin or clindamycin, both of which are active against the most common organisms and have good soft tissue penetration.

Women do not have as well-developed veins as men on their peripheral limbs. Therefore, injecting is more difficult and when there is no further venous access some women resort to skin popping. The trauma of repeated injecting into the subcutaneous tissues can cause ulcers and low grade infection (Fig. 4.1).

Fig. 4.1: Effects of repeated injection into subcutaneous tissues

During pregnancy, women's veins do become more prominent due to higher circulating hormone levels, with the breast veins developing more so. The breast veins are unable to tolerate venepuncture and become easily infected or the puncture site becomes necrotic (Fig. 4.2).

Fig. 4.2: Breast abscess due to injecting

Skin necrosis with super infection can occur with extravazation of the injected drug into the surrounding tissues. This can lead on to the most serious of subcutaneous infections, necrotising fascitis.

More serious infections require hospitalisation with culturing of a swab taken from the infected area. Blood cultures should also be taken before the commencement of intravenous antibiotics.

Subcutaneous infection can cause septic emboli which result in septic pulmonary infarcts. When this condition co-exists with endocarditis, mortality can be up to 16 per cent. The tricuspid valve is most frequently affected in drug misusers and the organism is usually *Staphylococcus aureus*. There should always be a high index of suspicion of endocarditis in an injecting drug user who has a fever, even without the classical evidence of a murmur or any local infected sites. There are very few drug users who can tolerate the six-week course of antibiotics and many discontinue this regime, being discharged on oral antibiotics. Valve replacement should be advised in those users with congestive cardiac failure, continual sepsis or repeated embolism, but would not be of any benefit in those who would continue to inject illicit drugs.

Septicaemia is caused by endocarditis in 40 per cent of cases in drug users. The majority occurs as a result of soft tissue infection in the groin area around the femoral vein – the most common site of primary infection. Other less common causes are mycotic aneurysms, septic arthritis, thrombophlebitis, pneumonia and osteomyelitis. The causative bacteria are *Staphylococcus aureus* and group A streptococci. Osteomyelitis occurs in injecting drug users by haematogenous seeding. *Pseudomonas aeruginosa* accounts for over three-quarters of all bone infections, mainly involving the vertebrae and pelvic girdle. Septic arthritis presents as a hot, swollen and painful joint on moving. Both require regular antibiotics over several weeks to resolve the infection.

Injecting drug users should ensure that they have adequate tetanus protection, as injecting paraphernalia could easily become contaminated in unhygienic conditions.

Trauma-induced injury from injecting drug misuse

Injecting into arm veins classically produces 'track' marks running down the length of the forearm. However, some users who have obliterated these veins through thrombophlebitis begin to use the femoral vein in the groin. Scars on the arms can heal over time and it could easily appear from a cursory medical examination that the user was not injecting. Looking more carefully at the groin site may show granulation tissue in someone who has only just begun injecting there, but this will eventually break down to leave a sinus communicating to the femoral vein. Constant use of this site invariably leads to the formation of a deep venous thrombosis (DVT), although the risk is substantially increased if gel-filled temazepam capsules are used as these can resolidify within the femoral vein. DVT is the most common cause of emergency hospital referral from the Maryland Center. Treatment commences with heparin initially until the diagnosis is confirmed, when the anti-coagulation therapy is changed to warfarin. A DVT presents with an intensely painful swollen leg and can be associated with pitting oedema. The aim of treatment is to prevent a fatal pulmonary embolism. Although users are often concerned that their leg is the more serious problem, the pain resolves with rest, analgesics and graduated support stockings. Long-term warfarin therapy can prove to be difficult in those with chaotic lifestyles and should be discontinued in those who continue to inject. Heparin would be used throughout the length of a pregnancy.

In those who have had recurrent bilateral DVTs, femoral vein areas may not be present and some women have used their femoral artery to continue injecting. Repeated puncture with a needle causes an aneurysm which, if discovered, requires emergency vascular surgery. This type of injecting is associated with a particular syndrome when temazepam is misused. 'Temazepam leg' is either caused by an allergic reaction to the temazepam capsule residue causing a vasculitis followed by secondary thrombosis, or the small arterioles are blocked by micro-emboli rendering areas of muscle ischaemia. This in turn produces massive rhabdomyolysis which can affect renal function. If fasciotomy is unsuccessful in treating the associated compartment syndrome the user will require amputation.

The use of other central venous sites such as subclavicular and supraclavicular veins can cause tension pneumothoraces, haemothoraces or pyopneumothoraces. Loss of the function of the voice has been reported after damage to the vagus or recurrent laryngeal nerves near the site of injection.

Harm minimisation

Harm minimisation is a health and social policy which prioritises the aim of decreasing the problems of drug misuse. Reducing these effects on health can be difficult, as drugs are illegal and their use covert, and some drug users consider the risks of criminal activity to fund their drug use more important than the considerable risks they take with their health.

Total abstinence is not an option for a majority of users who wish to continue taking drugs for whatever reason. Ensuring that they are able to use drugs in a safer manner protects the individual and society. The UK Government's response to the advent of HIV was expressed by the Advisory Committee on Drugs Misuse in 1988 who recommended a hierarchy of goals in harm minimisation:

1 The cessation of sharing of injecting equipment.

2 A move away from injectable to oral drug use.

3 A reduction in the quantity of drugs consumed.

4 Abstinence.

The first goal was achieved by the opening of Needle and Syringe Exchanges (NSE) in 1986. These schemes aim to reduce the need to share injection equipment, so limiting the spread of the viral transmissible diseases HIV and hepatitis B. Clean and sterile injecting equipment helps protect the individual user and also the community within which they live. NSEs also provide for the safe disposal of contaminated equipment and injecting paraphernalia, information on HIV and sexual health matters, free condoms and referral to drug treatment agencies. Some, similar to the Maryland Center, offer primary health care and safer drug use advice.

Some problems related to the injecting use of drugs are due to poor technique. Users are advised to use a quick release tourniquet which must be released after venepuncturing a suitable vein and before injecting the drug. Some users do not clean their skin prior to injecting, or use saliva, and so alcohol wipes are issued. The licking of needles to remove subcutaneous fat tissues after an unsuccessful attempt to venepuncture is discouraged. Users are instructed on the appropriate size of needle to use and to inject in the direction of the flow of blood. Some users repeatedly fill their syringes with blood in the belief that they are ensuring that all the drug is injected (flushing) but this generally leads to loss of blood around the vessel, leading to fibrosis and phlebitis and so reducing the available veins for further access.

It is hoped that regular contact with NSE staff encourages beneficial behavioural change and facilitates the earlier contact with drug treatment agencies, so shortening the length of time a user is on illicit drugs.

The other goals in harm minimisation are addressed by drug rehabilitation and treatment programmes. Originally the provision of methadone maintenance programmes was limited within the UK, with users in some regions having no access to methadone whatsoever. The situation has improved to such an extent now that there is generally a service prescribing methadone within any district of England and Wales.

Sources

Advisory Council on the Misuse of Drugs (1988). AIDS and Drug Misuse, Part 1. London: HMSO.

Banks, A., Waller, T.A.N. (Eds). (1988). Drug Misuse: A Practical Handbook for GPs. Oxford: Blackwell Scientific Publication.

Blenheim Project (1990). Changing Gear: A Book for Women who Use Drugs Illegally. London: The Blenheim Project/Mental Health Foundation.

El-Palil, A., Bhatacharyya, M. (1994). 'Widespread cutaneous atrophic lesions - signs of an ex-drug user', British Journal of Sexual Medicine, Vol. 21 (July.August), pp.35-36.

Hepburn, M. (1992). 'Socially Related Disorders: Drug Addiction, Maternal Smoking and Alcohol Consumption.' In: Calder, A.A., Dunlop, W. (Eds) High-Risk Pregnancy. Oxford: Butterworth-Heinemann.

Lart, R., Stimson, G.V, (1990). 'National survey of syringe exchange schemes in England', British Journal of Addiction, Vol. 85, pp.1433-44.

Moustoukas, N.M., Nichols, R.L., Smith, J.W., Garey, R.E., Egan, R.R. (1983). 'Contaminated street heroin: relationship to clinical infections', Archives of Surgery, Vol. 118, pp.746-49.

O'Hare, P.A., Newcombe, R., Matthews, A., Buning, E.C., Drucker, E. (Eds) (1992). The Reduction of Drug-Related Harm. London: Routledge.

Reichman, LB., Felton, C.P., Edsall, J.R. (1979). 'Drug dependence: a possible new risk factor for Tuberculosis disease', Archives of Internal Medicine, Vol. 139, pp.337-39.

Rementeria, J.L. (Ed.) (1977). Drug Abuse in Pregnancy and Neonatal Effects. Saint Louis: CV Mosby Company.

Scott, R.N., Going, J., Woodburn, K.R., Gilmour, P.G., Reid, D.B., Leiberman, D.P., Maraj, B., Pollock, J.G. (1992). 'Intra-arterial temazepam', British Medical Journal, Vol. 304, p.1630.

Strang, J. and Farrell, M. (1992). 'Harm minimization for drug users: when second best may be first', British Medical Journal, Vol. 304, pp.1127-28.

Chapter 5

OBSTETRIC PROBLEMS FOR DRUG USERS

Colette Sparey & Steve Walkinshaw

Dr Colette Sparey was a Registrar in Obstetrics and Gynaecology at the Liverpool Women's Hospital. She qualified in July 1987 at Manchester University and has worked primarily in obstetrics and gynaecology since then. She is currently subspeciality trainee in fetal medicine at the Royal Victoria Hospital, Newcastle.

Mr Steve Walkinshaw is currently consultant in Maternal Fetal Medicine at the Liverpool Women's Hospital, which is one of only two Trusts solely devoted to the care of women. Clinically he is a trained subspecialist in Fetal Medicine and responsible for the provision of specialist care in Liverpool and the North West region. He was involved in the Joint Colleges forum on Changing Childbirth and on the NHS Executive Group discussing joint educational initiatives. As Clinical Director he was actively involved in the developing of the Changing Childbirth model for implementation within Liverpool. His clinical interests are prenatal diagnosis, intrapartum care and late pregnancy antenatal monitoring.

The incidence of drug misuse has been rising for some time, with particularly steep increases occurring at the beginning of each of the last three decades.[1] Information regarding drug misuse is often difficult to obtain with any accuracy, the illegality of both the possession and use of these substances making people unwilling to admit to their habits. Nevertheless, the number of registered heroin addicts continues to rise.

In recent years there has been a change in the type of drugs misused, with a move away from heroin towards the use of pharmaceutical products and poly-drug use.[2] Drug misuse has increased disproportionately in women and is now almost equal to that in the male population and, thus, since the majority of drug abusers are young (i.e. in their teens and twenties), a substantial number of the drug misusers will be women of childbearing age.

Although the socio-economic background and lifestyle of these women is not specific to pregnancy, consequences may be expected. For example, they may be socially isolated and have housing, economic or domestic problems. Their lifestyle is often chaotic: attempts to finance and feed their habit can result in self-neglect and poor diet and may cause them to resort to prostitution and petty crime (it is estimated that the average heroin addict gets through £30,000 worth of heroin per annum). Prostitution and other criminal activity not only have legal implications but, in the case of the former, have serious implications for the woman's health with 'side effects' ranging from sexually transmitted infections such as gonorrhoea, chlamydia, hepatitis B and HIV infection to the risk of physical violence.

However dismal the potential picture, it is important to remember that many drug users lead perfectly normal lives, some holding down a job, many running a family and the majority differing little from their non-drug-using peers.[1]

In the following pages some of the impact of drug misuse in pregnancy is outlined. For more detailed effects on children please refer to Chapter 6.

Opiates

The opiates most commonly used are heroin (diacetylmorphine) and methadone. Heroin is derived from morphine, a naturally occurring opiate found in the poppy, papaver somniferum, whilst methadone is a synthetic drug. Heroin is more soluble than most other opiates and is therefore absorbed more rapidly into the central nervous system giving a quicker and more intense 'high' to the user, hence it is the drug of choice for most addicts. Methadone on the other hand is more slowly absorbed, has a longer half life and thus produces more stable blood levels, making it a suitable drug for treating addicts who are trying to 'kick the habit'.

Maternal effects

Amenorrhoea is common among opiate addicts, possibly mediated through a decreased production of gonadotrophins. Accurate dating of the pregnancy is therefore difficult, not only because of the irregular menstrual cycle but also because these women tend to book late in pregnancy, if at all. At these stages even ultrasound dating will be inaccurate.

Nutrition amongst addicts is poor and thus anaemia and various vitamin deficiencies, including of B6, folate and thiamine, are common. This problem is often aggravated during the first trimester by hyperemesis which may persist throughout pregnancy.

Opiate addicts who are using the drug intravenously will be at risk of a variety of unusual infections including bacterial endocarditis, thrombophlebitis, pneumonia, bronchitis and, if sharing needles, there is the risk of hepatitis B and HIV infection. Both past and current intravenous use of drugs may affect maternal venous access. Thrombosis of peripheral veins, caused by repeated intravenous injection of impure heroin and possibly by the use of dirty needles causing infective thrombophlebitis, makes the insertion of cannulae and the taking of blood for investigations difficult if not impossible. Another 'side effect' of prolonged opiate abuse is tolerance to its effects which, in the context of pregnancy and labour is most relevant to its analgesic qualities. Much higher doses are necessary during labour to achieve the same effect as in a non-drug user; alternatively epidural analgesia may be an option since this will be as effective as in the general population.

Fetal effects

The incidence of multiple pregnancies is thought to be increased although the exact mechanism is unknown. It may be related to a direct effect of opiates on ovarian function, causing dizygotic twinning. The incidence of congenital malformations is not increased by the use of opiates alone, before or during pregnancy.

Problems specific to pregnancy include an increased risk of antepartum haemorrhage due both to abruptio placentae and placenta praevia. The incidences of gestational hypertension and breech presentation are also reported to be increased.[3, 4] Whether these complications are a specific effect of opiates or more a reflection of the woman's general health and socio-economic circumstances is difficult to ascertain. The two most consistently reported findings are of a higher incidence of preterm deliveries and small-for-gestational-age babies,[5, 6, 7, 8, 9, 10, 11] up to 20 per cent in some series. Most studies also report an increase in intrauterine and neonatal deaths.[4, 9, 12, 13] Intrauterine deaths may be related to repeated episodes of withdrawal caused by erratic drug consumption by the mother. These episodes lead to intrauterine hypoxia which, if severe, results in intrauterine death. However, recent evidence in acute withdrawal programmes does not support this.[14] The aetiology of the increase in preterm labour is unclear. It may be related to increases in genital infection, a well-established cause of preterm labour[15, 16, 17, 18, 19, 20] and therefore closely linked with lifestyle.

Fetal assessment may be difficult since opiates are known to alter non-stress tests by reducing baseline variability and causing loss of accelerations. Opiates also suppress fetal breathing movements; thus whether these findings are drug related or an indication of genuine fetal compromise is difficult to deduce in the individual case. Fetal movements are also affected by opiates in particular; withdrawal causes an increase in fetal activity about 30 minutes after the onset of maternal symptoms.[21] Considerable care needs to be exercised if labour is prolonged, as withdrawal of the woman's normal opiate dose may provoke fetal withdrawal and unusual fetal heart rate patterns.

Neonatal effects

The effects of maternal opiate addiction on the newborn and infant need to be considered. Apart from the complications of preterm delivery and low birthweight to which these neonates are more prone, there is the risk of Neonatal Abstinence Syndrome (NAS), or withdrawal.

The symptoms to look for include:

- Tremor
- Sweating
- Irritability
- Fever

- High pitched cry
- Sneezing
- Respiratory distress
- Hyperactivity

- Vomiting
- Convulsions
- Hypertonicity
- Diarrhoea

The majority of symptoms appear within 24 to 48 hours of birth, but they have been reported up to six days after delivery.[9] Whether the onset, severity or duration of NAS is loosely related to the dose of opiate taken by the mother is uncertain. Some studies have found no correlation[13, 22] while others find the opposite.[23, 24, 25] Methadone can cause more severe and prolonged withdrawal symptoms and delayed reactions may be more common.[9, 12, 23] If taken in conjunction with diazepam the onset of symptoms may again be delayed.[26]

The risk of Sudden Infant Death Syndrome is five times greater in this group of infants.[10, 27] Developmental delay may be more common[28] and there is also the risk of being orphaned by maternal death due to either accidental or deliberate overdose, infection including HIV/AIDS or trauma.

Cocaine

Cocaine is an alkaloid derived from the coca plant. The water-soluble salt form can be absorbed through any mucosal surface (e.g. 'snorting') while a free cocaine base, 'crack', can be smoked, the latter being highly addictive and dangerous. The drug is a powerful vasoconstrictor and has been reported to be associated with maternal hypertension, spontaneous abortion and placental abruption.[29, 30, 31, 32] It has also been reported to be associated with small-for-gestational-age infants[33, 34, 35, 36, 37, 38] and this may be mediated through its appetite-suppressing effect[39] which also causes poor maternal weight gain.

Maternal effects

Maternal blood pressure and uterine vascular resistance are both increased while uterine blood flow is decreased by the use of cocaine.[40] This response appears to be enhanced in pregnancy, possibly mediated by progesterone.[41]

The incidence of arterial thromboses is also increased and this may be due to the reduced levels of protein C and antithrombin III found in these women.[42]

Maternal deaths have been reported due to:

- cardiac arrhythmias
- coronary ischaemia
- ruptured intracranial aneurysms
- intracerebral haemorrhage
- convulsions from raised blood pressure.

Fetal effects

Both the spontaneous and induced abortion rates are increased by cocaine addiction.[29, 33] The incidence of abruption is reported to be raised and the stillbirth rate from abruption is increased tenfold,[34] possibly due to damage to placental/uterine vessels early in pregnancy.

Animal studies report numerous different malformations and there have been similar reports from human studies.[43, 44] However, others report no increase in the incidence of congenital anomalies.[33, 45, 46] It is thought that the induced structural defects are not limited to the period of organogenesis but extend further into fetal life. Alteration or reduction in uterine and hence placental and fetal blood flow in the second trimester may cause vascular disruptions such as intestinal atresia, limb reduction defects and genitourinary defects.[47]

Intrauterine growth retardation (IUGR) is the most consistent finding in all studies. It is interesting to note that, unlike IUGR caused by opiate addiction, there does not appear to be 'head sparing'; that is, brain growth is impaired as well.[48, 37] Fat stores are reduced as is lean body mass and this may be due to impairment of nutrient transfer.[49] If cocaine use is stopped before delivery, there may be some resumption of growth. However, neurobehavioural defects may still persist.[50]

The incidence of prematurity is increased[33, 36] but this is less clear than with opiates.

Neonatal effects

There is some debate as to whether these actually exist. If they do, the symptoms are:

- hypertonia
- hyperactive startle reflex
- tachypnoea
- loose stools
- reduced sleep.[38]

One interesting finding is that if the woman uses cocaine as well as opiates, the NAS associated with opiate abuse is less severe.[51]

Benzodiazepines

Benzodiazepines are one of the most commonly prescribed types of drugs in Britain and are very easily obtainable, especially temazepam. The effects of these drugs on pregnancy are uncertain but the use of diazepam in early pregnancy has been associated with an increased incidence of cleft palate, and doses of more than 30mg per day may result in neonatal withdrawal,[52] the symptoms being:

- hypotonia
- hypothermia
- hyperbilirubinaemia
- feeding difficulties with poor sucking
- respiratory difficulties with episodes of apnoea.

As mentioned above, the concomitant use of benzodiazepines and opiates causes delay in the onset of neonatal abstinence syndrome associated with opiate abuse in pregnancy.

Amphetamines

Amphetamines are sympathomimetic drugs and are used most commonly for weight loss, since they are appetite suppressants, and for the treatment of narcolepsy as they are central nervous system (CNS) stimulants. Their use in pregnancy is not uncommon, often in association with other drugs.

There is little evidence regarding either specific or nonspecific effects in pregnancy. They do not appear to cause fetal anomalies but may be associated with an increase in small-for-gestational-age and preterm infants.[53]

Specific maternal effects which are not confined to pregnancy are hypertension, tachycardia and hyperthermia and thus the incidence of cerebrovascular accidents, myocardial infarction and cardiac arrhythmias may be increased in those with underlying pathology.

Marijuana

The effect of marijuana is uncertain. It is used most commonly together with tobacco and alcohol and thus it is difficult to identify effects specific to this drug.

Organisation of care

Drug abusers can be identified among women attending for antenatal care by screening urine samples for drug metabolites. However, this is time consuming and may not be cost effective except perhaps in those areas where the incidence of drug abuse is particularly high. Ethically, without express consent, this sort of screening is highly dubious practice.

We are more likely to succeed in our aims, and women are more likely to cooperate, if a 'team approach' is used, providing a comprehensive range of services including medical, social, psychological and psychiatric help with confidentiality guaranteed. This multidisciplinary approach should be maintained throughout pregnancy, delivery and the postpartum period, not only for the woman but also for her infant and immediate family.[54] Where possible, all drug-addicted pregnant patients should book under the care of an obstetric consultant within a unit who has declared a special interest in this problem. In addition, the involvement of a specially-trained midwife will ensure continuity, and hopefully coordination, of care between hospital and community staff enabling those who fail to attend their hospital visits to be followed up outside the hospital setting by someone familiar with their case/care. Registration of these women with the local drug unit will enable close monitoring of their drug-using habits during and after the pregnancy and provide an invaluable source of advice and support to both patient and professionals. Involvement of the GP is important, where the woman wishes it, and good channels of communication between consultant, GP, midwife and members of the drug unit staff should prevent confusion over management plans for individual patients.

Antenatal care

The aim of antenatal care for any pregnant woman is to ensure the safe delivery of a healthy mother and child. To ensure this for women who are drug users will require more input from all staff involved than would be necessary for the usually fit and healthy pregnant population.

Screening

In addition to the usual screening tests, there are a number of other tests which may be indicated in this group. These women are prone to sexually transmitted infections.[23] From April 2000 the Department of Health has advised that all pregnant women should be offered screening for hepatitis B surface antigen, and, where indicated, swabs may be taken for sexually transmitted infections. The question of screening for HIV is fraught with difficulties. Another important investigation is an ultrasound scan for gestational age. In units where it is not policy to perform this for all pregnant women, an exception should be made for drug users since their gestational age based on the last menstrual period is so unreliable. For those women who 'book late', parameters more accurate in late pregnancy, such as foot length and transcerebellar diameter, may be necessary.

Drug use

The aim should be to encourage a decrease or even total cessation of drug use. Where possible, transfer to legal alternatives is preferable to continued use of street drugs. At present this is only possible for heroin addicts where the legal alternative is methadone. Transfer on to this drug has many potential advantages.

The institution of a methadone maintenance programme brings the mother into contact with both medical and social support which may improve her standard of living sufficiently to benefit both her health and that of her child.[55] It ensures contact is maintained with medical services, as this is necessary to obtain a regular supply of the drug. It should reduce the incidence of withdrawal because the supply is constant and methadone is taken at regular intervals, abolishing the normal peaks and troughs which occur with heroin use.[56] This in turn should reduce the incidence of fetal withdrawal, meconium staining of liquor and intrauterine deaths.[23]

The dose of methadone will need adjusting during pregnancy. Initially, conversion to methadone from heroin is needed if this has not already been done prior to pregnancy. This requires the experience and skill of those professionals who work in this field on a daily basis. Once stabilised on methadone, consideration can be given to reducing the dose. If this is to be done it should be done slowly at a rate of no more than 5mg reductions per week. Often it is possible to reduce the dose in the second trimester only to find that it needs increasing again later in pregnancy because of the altered pharmacokinetics of the drug caused by pregnancy physiology.[57]

The disadvantage of maintenance on methadone is that it has a much longer half life than heroin. This means that neonatal withdrawal symptoms are more severe, and can also be delayed and last longer.[9, 12, 23] Unfortunately, there is no legal substitute for cocaine or any of the other drugs of abuse. The only option in these cases (when and if the women admit to their use) is to persuade them to reduce or cease their intake.

Drug use can be monitored during pregnancy, and at any other time, by testing urine for drug metabolites, with maternal consent.

Fetal monitoring

Fetal growth is a major concern in these women, the majority of whom not only use illicit drugs but also smoke tobacco which causes a dose-related reduction in birthweight.[58] Regular antenatal checks are necessary and serial ultrasound measurements for growth are advisable. As with any other pregnant woman, advice should be given regarding fetal movements in the third trimester.

Labour and delivery

The fact that a woman is known to be a drug user should have little if any effect on her management during labour or afterwards, with a few exceptions.

Women who have used drugs intravenously are likely to have poor venous access which may cause problems if faced with an intrapartum emergency. Similarly adequate analgesia can be difficult to provide in both opiate and cocaine addicts especially if the analgesic chosen is an opiate. Much higher doses than normal may be required and even then may not be effective. Epidural analgesia is an alternative in those women who find this acceptable.

Intrapartum fetal monitoring may be difficult due to the effects of opiates on fetal heart rate patterns. There may be reduced baseline variability, loss of accelerations and, as mentioned above, intrapartum fetal withdrawal may result in unusual CTG patterns, all of which make interpretation of cardiotocographs difficult.

Other complications of pregnancy described above will dictate the management of specific cases during labour as with any other pregnancy. The management of HBSAg and HIV positive women should be as for any other woman so affected. Although drug users are more likely to be positive for these infections, management of any situation where contact with body fluids is likely should be one of great care, regardless of a person's admitted drug habits, and should follow established guidelines.

Ongoing care

Pregnancy is a unique episode in a woman's life and, as such, should be 'exploited' as an opportunity to encourage change in the woman's lifestyle to eliminate habits which are potentially dangerous, not just for her baby, but also for herself. The use of illicit drugs during pregnancy is dangerous for both mother and child. The risk does not necessarily diminish after birth. The most important factor in long-term success in breaking an addictive habit is a change in lifestyle[59] and thus support after delivery from the appropriately qualified personnel is imperative.

References

1 Ministerial Group on the Misuse of Drugs (1988). Tackling Drug Misuse. A Summary of the Government's Strategy (3rd edition). London: Home Office.

2 Hepburn, M. (1992). 'Socially related disorders: Drug addiction, maternal smoking and alcohol consumption.' In: Calder, A.A., Dunlop, W. (Eds). High Risk Pregnancy. Oxford: Butterworth-Heinemann.

3 Silver, H., Wapner, R., Loriz-Vega, M., Finnegan, L.P. (1987). 'Addiction in pregnancy: high risk intrapartum management and outcome', Journal of Perinatology, Vol. 7(3), pp.178-84.

4 Finnegan, L.P. (1982). 'Outcome of children born to women dependent on narcotics'. In: Stimmel, B. (Ed.). The Effects of Maternal Alcohol and Drug Abuse on the Newborn. New York: Haworth Press.

5 Thornton, L., Clune, M., Maguire, R., Griffin, E., O'Connor, J. (1990). 'Narcotic addiction: the expectant mother and her baby', Irish Medical Journal, Vol. 83(4), pp.139-42.

6 Chasnoff, I.J., Burns, K.A., Burns, W.T., Scholl, S.H. (1986). 'Prenatal drug exposure: effects on neonates' and infants' growth and development', Neurotoxicol-Teratol, Vol. 9(4), pp.311-13.

7 Kaltenbach, K., Finnegan, L.P. (1987). 'Perinatal and developmental outcome of infants exposed to methadone inutero', Neurotoxicol-Teratol, Vol. 9(4), pp.311-13.

8 Klenka, H.M. (1986). 'Babies born in a district general hospital to mothers taking heroin', British Medical Journal, Vol. 293, pp.745-46.

9 Perlmutter, J. (1974). 'Heroin addiction and pregnancy', Obstetric Gynaecology Survey, Vol. 29, pp.439-46.

10 Ellwood, D.S., Sutherland, P., Kent, C., O'Connor, M. (1987). 'Maternal narcotic addiction: pregnancy outcome in patients managed by a specialised drug dependency antenatal clinic', Australia and New Zealand Journal of Obstetric Gynaecology, Vol. 27, pp.92-98.

11 Gregg, J.E.M., Davidson, D.C., Weindling, A.M. (1988). 'Inhaling heroin during pregnancy: effects on the baby', British Medical Journal, Vol. 296, p.754.

12 Blinick, G., Wallach, R.C., Jerez, E., Ackerman, B.D. (1976). 'Drug addicition in pregnancy and the neonate', American Journal of Obstetric Gynaecology, Vol. 125, pp.135-42.

13 Fricker, H.S., Segal, S. (1978). 'Narcotic addiction, pregnancy and the newborn', American Journal of Disabled Children, Vol. 132, pp.360-66.

14 Hepburn, M., Forrest, C.A. (1988). 'Does infection with HIV affect the outcome of pregnancy?', British Medical Journal, Vol. 296, p.934.

15 Salafia, C.M., Vogel, C.A., Vintzileos, A.M., Bantham, K.F., Pezzullo, J., Silberman, L. (1991). 'Placental pathological findings in preterm birth', American Journal of Obstetric Gynaecology, Vol. 165, pp.934-38.

16 Schwartz, P., Pattinson, R.C., Deale, J., Carstens, A. (1989). 'Subclinical chorioamnionitic infection in preterm deliveries', Proceedings of the Eighth Conference in Priorities in Perinatal Care, Mpekweni, Ceskei, South Africa, pp.42-43.

17 Armer, T.L., Duff, P. (1991). 'Intraamniotic infection in patients with intact membranes and preterm labour', Obstetric Gynaecology Survey, Vol. 46, pp.589-93.

18 Krohn, M.A., Hillier, S.I., Lee, M.L., Rabe, L.K., Eschenbach, D.A. (1991). 'Vaginal bacteroides species are associated with an increased rate of preterm delivery among women in preterm labour', Journal of Infectious Diseases, Vol. 164, pp.88-93.

19 McGregor, J.A., French, J.I., Richter, R. et al. (1991). 'Antenatal microbiologic and maternal risk factors associated with prematurity', American Journal of Obstetric Gynaecology, Vol. 163, pp.1465-73.

20 McDonald, H.M., O'Loughlin, J.A., Vignewaran, R., McDonald, P.J. (1991). 'Vaginal infection and preterm labour', British Journal of Obstetric Gynaecology, Vol. 98, pp.427-35.

21 Robins, L.N., Mills, J.L., Krulewitch, C., Allen, A.H. (1993). 'Effects of in utero exposure to street drugs', American Journal of Public Health, Vol. 83 (Supplement), pp.6-32.

22 Mack, G., Thomas, D., Giles, W., Buchanan, N. (1991). 'Methadone levels and neonatal withdrawal', Journal of Paediatrics, Childcare and Health, Vol. 27, No. 2, pp.96-100.

23 Strauss, M.E., Andresko, M., Styker, J.C., Wardell, J.N., Dunkel, L.D. (1974). 'Methadone maintenance during pregnancy: pregnancy, birth and neonatal characteristics', American Journal of Obstetric Gynaecology, Vol. 120, pp.895-900.

24 Doberczak, T.M., Kandall, S.R., Wilets, I. (1991). 'Neonatal opiate abstinence syndrome in term and preterm infants', Journal of Paediatrics, Vol. 118, No. 6, pp.933-37.

25 Harper, R.G., Solish, G., Feingol, E. et al. (1977). 'Maternal ingested methadone, body fluid methadone and neonatal withdrawal syndrome', American Journal of Obstetric Gynaecology, Vol. 129, pp.417-24.

26 Sutton, L.R., Hinterliter, S.A. (1990). 'Diazepam abuse in pregnant women on methadone maintenance: implications for the neonate', Clin. Paediatr. Phila., Vol. 29, No. 2, pp.108-11.

27 Rajegouda, B.K., Kandal, J.R., Falcighia, H. (1978). 'Sudden infant deaths in infants of narcotic-dependent mothers', Early Human Development, Vol. 2, pp.219-25.

28 Oloffson, M., Buckley, W., Anderson, G.E. and Friis-Hansen, B. (1983). 'Investigation of 89 children born to drug-dependent mothers. II. Follow up 1-10 years after birth', Acta Paediatrica Scandinavica, Vol. 72, pp.407-10.

29 Chasnoff, I.J., Burns, W.J., Schnoll, S.H., Burns, K.A. (1985). 'Cocaine use in pregnancy', New England Journal of Medicine, Vol. 313, pp.666-69.

30 Smith, C.G., Deitch, K.V. (1987). 'Cocaine: a maternal, fetal and neonatal risk', Journal of Paediatric Health Care, Vol. 1, pp.120-24.

31 Acker, D., Sachs, B., Tracey, K., Wise, W. (1983). 'Abruptio placentae associated with cocaine use', American Journal of Obstetric Gynaecology, Vol. 146, No. 2, pp.220-1.

32 Macgregor, S., Keith, L., Chasnoff, I., Rosner, M., Chisom, G., Shaw, P., Minogue, J. (1987). 'Cocaine use during pregnancy: adverse perinatal outcome', American Journal of Obstetric Gynaecology, Vol. 157, pp.686-90.

33 Gillogley, K.M., Evans, A.T., Hansen, R.L. et al. (1990). 'The perinatal impact of cocaine, amphetamine and opiate use detected by universal intrapartum screening', American Journal of Obstetric Gynaecology, Vol. 163, pp.1535-42.

34 Bingol, N., Fuchs, M., Diaz, V. et al. (1987). 'Tertaogenicity of cocaine in humans', Journal of Paediatrics, Vol. 110, pp.93-96.

35 Chouteau, M., Namerow, P.B., Leppert, P. (1988). 'The effect of cocaine abuse on birth weight and gestational age', Obstetric Gynaecology, Vol. 72, pp.351-54.

36 Little, B.B., Snell, L.M., Klein, V.R. et al. (1989). 'Cocaine abuse during pregnancy: maternal and fetal implications', Obstetric Gynaecology, Vol. 73, pp.157-60.

37 Zuckerman, B., Frank, D.A., Hingson, R. et al. (1989). 'Effects of maternal marijuana and cocaine on fetal growth', New England Journal of Medicine, Vol. 320, pp.762-68.

38 Fulroth, R., Phillips, B., Durand, D. (1989). 'Perinatal outcome of infants exposed to cocaine and/or heroin in utero', American Journal of Dis. in Child., Vol. 143, pp.905-10.

39 Riley, D. (1987). 'The management of the pregnant drug addict', Bulletin of the Royal College of Psychiatrists, Vol. 11, pp.362-65.

40 Woods, J.R., Plessinger, M.A., Clark, K.E. (1987). 'Effect of cocaine on uterine blood flow and fetal oxygenation', JAMA, Vol. 257, pp.957-61.

41 Woods, J.R., Plessinger, M.A. (1990). 'Pregnancy increases cardiovascular toxicity to cocaine', American Journal of Obstetric Gynaecology, Vol. 162, pp.529-33.

42 Choksi, S.K., Miller, G., Ronione, A. et al. (1989). 'Cocaine and cardiovascular diseases: the leading edge', Cardiology, Vol. 3, pp.1-6.

43 Mahalik, M.P., Gautieri, R.F., Mann, D.E. (1980). 'Teratogenic potential of cocaine hydrocholoride in CF-1 mice', Journal of Pharmacological Science, Vol. 69, pp.703-706.

44 Mahalik, M.P., Gautieri, R.F., Mann, D.E. (1984). 'Mechanisms of cocaine-induced teratogenesis', Res Commun Substance Abuse, Vol. 5, pp.279-302.

45 Fantel, A.G., MacPhail, B.J. (1982). 'The teratogenicity of cocaine', Teratology, Vol. 26, pp.17-19.

46 Church, M.W., Dintcheff, B.A., Gessner, P.K. (1988). 'Dose-dependent consequences of cocaine on pregnancy outcome in the Long-Evans rat', Neurotoxicology and Teratology, Vol. 10, pp.51-58.

47 Hoyme, H.E., Jones, K.L., Dixon, S.D. et al. (1990). 'Prenatal cocaine exposure and vascular disruption', Paediatrics, Vol. 85, pp.743-47.

48 Little, B.B., Snell, L.M. (1991). 'Brain growth among fetuses exposed to cocaine in utero: asymmetrical growth retardation', Obstetric Gynaecology, Vol. 77, pp.361-64.

49 Frank, D.A., Bauchner, H., Parker, S. et al. (1990). 'Neonatal body proportionality and body composition after in utero exposure to cocaine and marijuana', Journal of Paediatrics, Vol. 117, pp.622-26.

50 Chasnoff, I.J., Griffith, D.R., Macgrgor, S. et al. (1989). 'Temporal patterns of cocaine use in pregnancy: perinatal outcome', JAMA, Vol. 261, pp.1741-44.

51 Finnegan, L., Kaltenbach, K., Weiner, S., Haney, B. (1990). 'Neonatal cocaine exposure: assessment of risk scale', Paediatr Res, Vol. 27, No. 10A Abstract.

52 Harrison, R. (1986). 'The use of non essential drugs, alcohol and cigarettes during pregnancy', Irish Medical Journal, Vol. 79, pp.338-41.

53 Oro, A.S., Dixon, S.P. (1987). 'Perinatal cocaine and methamphetamine exposure: maternal and neonatal correlates', New England Journal of Medicine, Vol. 297, pp.528-30.

54 Leif, N.R. (1985). 'The drug user as a parent', International Journal of Addictions, Vol. 20, pp.63-97.

55 Rosner, M.A., Keith, L., Chasnoff, I.J. (1982). 'Western University Dependence Programme: the impact of intensive prenatal care on labour and delivery outcomes', American Journal of Obstetric Gynaecology, Vol. 144, pp.23-27.

56 Finnegan, L.P. (1991). 'Treatment issues for opioid dependent women during the perinatal period', Journal of Psychoactive Drugs, Vol. 23, No. 2, pp.191-201.

57 Pond, S.M., Kreek, M.J., Tong, T.G., Raghoutath, J., Berowitz, N.L. (1985). 'Altered methadone pharmokinetics in methadone maintained pregnant women', Journal of Pharmacological Experimental Therapy, Vol. 233, pp.1-6.

58 Kline, J., Stein, Z., Hutzler, M. (1987). 'Cigarettes, alcohol and marijuana: varying associations with birthweight', International Journal of Epidemiology, Vol. 16, pp.44-51.

59 Oppenheimer, E., Stimson, G.V., Thorley, A. (1979). 'Seven year follow up of heroin addicts: abstinence and continued use compared', British Medical Journal, Vol. 2, pp.627-30.

Chapter 6

MATERNAL DRUG USE: CONSEQUENCES FOR THE CHILD

Ben Shaw

Ben Shaw qualified as a doctor in Birmingham in
1980. He has been a consultant neonatologist at the
Liverpool Women's Hospital since 1991. His main
interests are neonatal respiratory disorders and the
outcomes of the babies of drug-dependent women.

A number of drugs, including opiates, cocaine, benzodiazepines, marijuana, alcohol and tobacco, when used by pregnant women have been reported to have effects on the fetus, the new-born infant and the child in later life. This chapter will deal with the drugs most commonly used in pregnancy and will discuss in particular the assessment of infants prone to drug withdrawal (neonatal abstinence syndrome (NAS)) and its treatment.

Opiates

An increased risk of placental abruption, withdrawal in utero, perinatal asphyxia, meconium aspiration, perinatal infection and malpresentation have all been reported in women dependent on opiates during pregnancy.[1] The incidences of low birth weight (less than 2.5 kg), prematurity and growth retardation are higher.[2,3,4,5,6,7,8] Although it has been suggested in the past that the incidence of respiratory distress syndrome may be decreased in those infants whose mothers have been taking opiates, it is possible that the incidence is similar to the normal population as there are a higher number of growth-retarded infants born to infants of opiate-dependent mothers.

A higher incidence of congenital abnormalities has been reported in infants of mothers who have taken opiates.[9] In particular there may be a higher incidence of facial and palatal clefting.[9] It has been suggested that babies born to women taking methadone tend to have a higher birth weight than those born to women taking heroin[5] although it is difficult to be certain of the degree of influence that other social factors, for example poor nutrition and social deprivation, may have and it may be that opiate use per se is not a major contributory factor to these effects.

Features of NAS have been extensively described and include hyperactivity, irritability, tremors, hypertonicity, dehydration, seizures, weight loss and aspiration.[10,11] The incidence of NAS requiring treatment in infants of mothers who have abused heroin has been reported to be approximately 40-85%.[6,7,12,13] Signs become evident at a mean age of 13 hours. The incidence of NAS may be lower in those infants whose mothers have smoked heroin.[14] The incidence of NAS requiring treatment in infants of mothers taking methadone is approximately 40% and generally presents within 72 hours of birth.[15] Reports in the literature generally suggest that the risk of NAS, its severity, duration and length of hospital stay are directly correlated with the dose of methadone being used.[16,17] However, studies which have investigated serum methadone levels have not always supported this.[18] The signs of NAS may persist for longer in infants exposed to methadone.[1] There have been anecdotal reports of a later withdrawal occurring at one to two weeks of age,[19] although in one recent controlled study there was no increased risk of signs in the methadone-exposed group compared to a control group.[15] There appears to be less risk of NAS if the infant is preterm[20] and there is a higher risk in Caucasians.

There is an increased risk of sudden infant death syndrome in infants born to opiate users.[9] A large study from New York reported that even when race, age, parity, cigarette smoking and birth weight were taken into account, the risk of sudden death in infants of both methadone and heroin using mothers was still high.[21]

Studies of short to medium term outcome have reported that more than 50% of infants of opiate users remain with their mothers.[6,7] A study from Chicago has reported a high incidence (30%) of abuse or neglect particularly when the offspring of opiate users become toddlers (the perpetrator of the abuse usually being one of the parents).[22] A number of small studies have reported lower IQ, higher anxiety levels, behaviour disorders, language difficulties and feelings of aggression and rejection in older children whose mothers abused opiates during pregnancy.[23,24,25] It is possible that many of these problems are related to other social factors and not to drug use per se; a study from Israel reported behaviour problems, hyperactivity and a lower developmental quotient in infants born to heroin-taking mothers and/or fathers. However, if infants were adopted early (thus being removed from some of the adversities of their social environment) these problems were no more common than in a control group.[26]

Cocaine

Cocaine use is widespread in the USA and is becoming more common in the United Kingdom, particularly owing to the availability of crack cocaine. Mothers taking cocaine are at increased risk of placental abruption and may be poorly nourished, resulting in poor fetal growth.[27] Infants born to mothers using cocaine are more likely to be born prematurely, to have low birth weight, to have low head circumference and to be growth retarded.[27,28,29,30,31] The risk of stillbirth is higher, usually secondary to placental abruption[27] and there may be an increased risk of congenital abnormalities and cranial and genitourinary defects (the latter possibly as a result of the vasoconstrictor effect of cocaine).[32,33] It has been suggested that infants are at increased risk of cerebral infarction although a study of cerebral ultrasound in infants born to cocaine-using mothers revealed no abnormalities[34] and a small study of cerebral blood flow in new borns exposed to cocaine showed no hypoperfusion although there were behavioural and EEG abnormalities.[35] It is likely that the majority of infants exposed to cocaine in utero escape significant ischaemic injury.[35] Behavioural abnormalities in the new-born period are more likely than in non-exposed infants, although these are probably due to a direct neurotoxic effect of cocaine metabolites rather than true NAS.[36] Whatever the cause, neurobehavioural abnormalities in the new born, usually presenting as tremor and hypertonia, are less likely with cocaine exposure compared to other drug exposure in utero.[37] Many infants exposed to cocaine in utero may exhibit excitable behaviour although some have depressed activity in the perinatal period (possibly as a result of intrauterine hypoxia).[38] Many mothers taking cocaine also abuse other drugs and the risk of signs of NAS appearing has been reported to increase if cocaine and heroin are used together.[29] Infants born to cocaine-using mothers are more likely to be admitted to the Neonatal Intensive Care Unit and to stay in hospital for longer.[31] The majority of the increased cost of caring for infants with cocaine exposure, however, is related to the increased risk of prematurity.[31]

There is an increased risk of sudden infant death syndrome in infants born to cocaine-using mothers but this does not appear to be as high as with opiate exposure in utero.[21] There have been a number of reports of infants and young children having impaired mental, psychomotor and behavioural scores after being exposed to cocaine in utero,[23,39,40] although one group has reported similar language and developmental achievements at 2 1/2 years when compared to a control group of infants not exposed to drugs.[41] It is difficult to be certain that the medium and long-term childhood effects attributed to cocaine exposure are not influenced by other confounding variables such as polydrug, alcohol and tobacco use in the mother as well as her nutritional state.

Benzodiazepines

There is very little literature regarding the effect of benzodiazepines on the fetus in utero. It has been suggested that birth weight may be lower in infants born to benzodiazepine-using mothers[42] and that there may be an increased risk of congenital malformations, particularly clefting.[9,43] However these effects may be related to other drug use, including alcohol, as women taking benzodiazepines are often polydrug users. Infants may be floppy at birth or exhibit NAS. The withdrawal may occur later than with opiates, starting at 7 to 14 days,[44] and usually resulting in an increase in the need for treatment. Withdrawal may persist for up to a month following its presentation. There may be an increased risk of sudden infant death in infants born to benzodiazepine users.[9]

Other substances

Chronic alcohol abuse can cause fetal alcohol syndrome and result in NAS with similar signs to those seen in infants who have been exposed to other drugs in utero.[45] The incidence of alcohol-related fetal and neonatal effects may be underestimated. Maternal smoking has a number of detrimental effects to the fetus and placenta which are beyond the scope of this chapter. In terms of neonatal behaviour, infants born to tobacco smokers may exhibit increased excitability when compared to controls. Infants born to mothers who have used marijuana may exhibit mild withdrawal but do not appear to have any longer lasting sequelae.[46]

Monitoring signs of withdrawal

The aims of managing an infant who is at risk of neonatal abstinence syndrome are:
- to maintain a normal temperature
- to ensure adequate sleep between feeds
- to reduce hyperactivity and excessive crying
- to reduce motor instability
- to ensure adequate weight gain.

Knowledge of the risk of abstinence syndrome should preclude the use of naloxone in infants with respiratory depression at birth as this may precipitate withdrawal signs. Naloxone is not used routinely at Liverpool Women's Hospital for any infant whose mother has received sedation, in case the mother is an unregistered drug user. A number of early assessment regimes of drug-withdrawing infants categorised signs into mild (infant tremulous), moderate (tremulous with excessive salivation, yawning, sneezing and loose stools) and severe (diarrhoea, vomiting and seizures in addition to moderate signs).[47] Other workers graded withdrawal depending on the degree of irritability from mild (grade 1) to marked irritability when disturbed (grade 2) to marked frequent irritability when undisturbed (grade 3).[48]

A major disadvantage of these grading systems is that they are rather subjective. In order to make assessment of the drug-withdrawing infant more objective, Finnegan et al assessed 20 signs commonly found in neonatal withdrawal, assigning each of them a number when present based on their severity.[10] The numbers were added and a total score was allocated to each infant. This system had a low inter-observer variability. Treatment for withdrawal was only prescribed when an infant reached a score of eight or more. The authors found that infants who had been assessed by the scoring system received less drug treatment and had a shorter hospital stay. It has been suggested that the system proposed by Finnegan and colleagues enables an estimation of clinical status, progression, and response to treatment to be made in the new-born infant. Indeed the 'Finnegan chart' is one of the most commonly used for assessing an infant with NAS particularly in the United Kingdom.[49] However, once members of staff have had experience in assessing infants with NAS it is possible that, even when charts are used, a large subjective element comes into play. Furthermore, it is not known which specific signs of NAS are predictive of later adverse outcome in these infants. At Liverpool Women's Hospital we have developed a simplified chart and assessment strategy which aims to treat signs of NAS that either cause distress or are potentially dangerous to the infant. Using our chart (Appendix 1), treatment should be considered if the baby has profuse watery stools or profuse vomiting or requires tube feeding due to incoordinate sucking. The only other indication for commencing treatment is if the infant has not settled after comforting, swaddling or use of a pacifier following two consecutive feeds. We do not advocate prescribing treatment for individual minor signs of drug withdrawal. It is important for staff to understand that withdrawal from opiates may occur early (under 24 hours), withdrawal from opioids may occur three to four days after birth and that polydrug use may delay or skew withdrawal signs.

Treatment of drug withdrawal

A recent survey of neonatal units in England and Wales revealed great diversity with regard to the different drugs used for treating NAS.[49] The aim of treatment is to stabilise the infant, suppress signs of abstinence syndrome and to restore the normal sucking and sleeping pattern of the infant. General measures such as cuddling, swaddling and using a pacifier may be effective. There is some evidence that nursing the infant on a water bed reduces the risk of NAS and the need for treatment.[50] It is also important to avoid excessive sedation.

There is very little objective evidence to support the use of any individual drug for the treatment of NAS. A recent systematic review identified 14 randomised trials of drug treatment for NAS.[51] In none of these were the carers blinded to the treatment received and in only five was the drug habit of the mother verified by urine analysis. The outcome measures assessed in these trials were mainly NAS scores (which may have had a subjective bias). Ability to suck adequately and developmental status at six months were each assessed in one trial. Owing to the range of drugs used to treat the NAS, it was not possible to subject these trials to a meta-analysis. The majority of these trials (n=11) assessed the use of paregoric, which is a mixture of morphine, alcohol, camphor, tincture of opium and benzoic acid. The use of diazepam was assessed in nine, and chlorpromazine, morphine and methadone were each assessed in one. The review concluded that treatment with morphine appeared to reduce symptom scores more than phenobarbitone or diazepam and that there was no difference between methadone and phenobarbitone or diazepam or chlorpromazine and diazepam. When an opiate was the main drug used in pregnancy, paregoric was more effective at controlling symptoms than phenobarbitone or diazepam. Furthermore there was concern that the latter two drug treatments may predispose to an increased risk of seizures either during their use or after stopping them. When there was polydrug usage in pregnancy, phenobarbitone appeared better at controlling signs. At six months, development was the same in groups of infants treated with diazepam, phenobarbitone or paregoric. It also appeared that paregoric improved coordination of the infants' suck whereas diazepam may have impaired this. Although some useful information can be obtained from the randomised controlled trials reviewed, none of them took into account the effects of variable antenatal care, maternal smoking, poverty, neglect and ill-health. Furthermore the subjectivity of the scoring systems used and the non-blinding of treatments used makes the assessment of the outcomes measured open to bias.

In Liverpool, NAS is initially treated with morphine sulphate (see Appendix). The baby is reviewed daily by the paediatric staff and the level of treatment is reduced every 24 hours if the baby is feeding well and settling better between feeds. If improvement does not occur, the infant is discussed with a senior paediatrician to assess whether other medication may be required. We generally treat the effects of benzodiazepine usage (which often shows up as later withdrawal), with diazepam – others have used clonazepam. With a biphasic withdrawal pattern consistent with polydrug use, we use phenobarbitone or chloral hydrate to ease the baby's distress over the withdrawal period. The majority of infants can be nursed on the postnatal wards and are kept in hospital for three days if they have not withdrawn, or until off all medication if they have received treatment for withdrawal. Rarely, as a result of either prolonged withdrawal or difficult social circumstances, the infant needs to be admitted to the neonatal unit.

Summary

Drug use in pregnancy may result in problems in the pregnancy and compromise of the fetus. The infant may exhibit NAS (drug withdrawal), the assessment of which may be extremely subjective. The best treatment appears to be morphine if the main drug used has been an opiate or opioid. If other drugs have been used alone or in combination, therapy may need to be individually tailored towards a longer or biphasic pattern of withdrawal. There is still an urgent need for simple objective measures of assessing drug withdrawal in the infant and for randomised controlled trials of different therapies for drug withdrawal.

References

1 Ostrea, E.M. Jr. (1978). The care of the drug dependent woman and her infant. Lansing, Michigan. Michigan Department of Public Health.

2 Lam, S.K., To, W.K., Duthie, S.J., Ma, H.K. (1992). 'Narcotic addiction in pregnancy with adverse maternal and perinatal outcome.' Aust NZJ Obstet Gynaecol, Vol. 32, pp.216-221.

3 Vance, J.C., Chant, D.C., Tudehope, D.I., Gray, P.H., Hayes, A.J. (1997). 'Infants born to narcotic dependent mothers: physical growth patterns in the first 12 months of life.' J Paediatr Child Health, Vol. 33, pp.504-508.

4 Boer, K., Smit, B.J., Van Huis, A.M., Hogerzeil, H.V. (1994). 'Substance use in pregnancy: do we care?' Acta Paediatr Suppl, Vol. 404, pp.65-71.

5 Olofsson, M., Buckley, W., Andersen, F., Friis-Hansen, B. (1983). 'Investigation of 89 children born by drug dependent mothers.' Acta Paediatr Scand, Vol. 72, pp.403-406.

6 Klenka, H.M. (1986). 'Babies born in a district general hospital to mothers taking heroin.' Br Med J, Vol. 293, pp.745-746.

7 Alroomi, L.G., Davidson, J., Evans, T.J., Galea, P., Howat, R. (1988). 'Maternal narcotic abuse and the newborn.' Arch Dis Child, Vol. 63, pp.81-83.

8 Lipsitz, P.J., Blatman, S. (1974). 'Newborn infants of mothers on methadone maintenance.' NY State J Med, pp.994-999.

9 Thomas, D.B. (1995). 'Cleft palate, mortality and morbidity in infants of substance abusing mothers.' J Paediatr Child Health, Vol. 31, pp.457-460.

10 Finnegan, L.P., Kron, R.E., Connaughton, J.F., Emich, J.P. (1975). 'Assessment and treatment of abstinence in the infant of the drug dependent mother.' Int J Clin Pharmacol, Vol. 12, pp.19-32.

11 American Academy of Pediatrics Committee on Drugs. (1983). 'Neonatal drug withdrawal.' Pediatrics, Vol. 72, pp.895-902.

12 Reddy, A M., Harper, R.G., Stern, G. (1971). 'Observations on heroin and methadone withdrawal in the newborn.' Pediatrics, Vol. 48, pp.353-358.

13 Zelson, C., Rubio, E., Wasserman, E. (1971). 'Neonatal narcotic addiction: 10 year observation.' Pediatrics, Vol. 48, pp.178-189.

14 Gregg, J.E.M., Davidson, D.C., Weindling, A.M. (1988). 'Inhaling heroin during pregnancy: effects on the baby.' Brit Med J, Vol. 296, p.754.

15 Shaw, N.J., McIvor, L. (1994). 'Neonatal abstinence syndrome after maternal methadone treatment.' Arch Dis Child, Vol. 71, pp.F203-F205.

16 Doberczak, T.M., Kandall, S.R., Friedmann, P. (1993). 'Relationship between maternal methadone dosage, maternal-neonatal methadone levels and neonatal withdrawal.' Obstet Gynecol, Vol. 81, pp.936-940.

17 Malpas, T.J., Darlow, B.A., Lennox, R., Horwood, L.T. (1995). Maternal methadone dosage and neonatal withdrawal.' Aust NZ J Obstet Gynaecol, Vol. 35, pp.175-177.

18 Mack, G., Thomas, D., Giles, W., Buchanan, N. (1991). 'Methadone levels and neonatal withdrawal.' J Paediatr Child Health, Vol. 27, pp.96-100.

19 Challis, R.E., Scopes, J.W. (1977). 'Late withdrawal symptoms in babies born to methadone addicts.' Lancet, Vol. 2, p.1230.

20 Doberczak, T.M., Kandall, S.R., Wilets, I. (1991). 'Neonatal opiate abstinence syndrome in term and preterm infants.' Pediatr, Vol. 118, pp.933-937.

21 Kandall, S.R., Gaines, J., Habel, L., Davidson, G., Jessop, D. (1993). 'Relationship of maternal substance abuse to subsequent sudden infant death syndrome in offspring.' J Pediatr, Vol. 123, pp.120-126.

22 Jandes, P.K., Ekwo, E., Van Voorhis, J. (1995). 'Association of drug abuse and child abuse.' Child Abuse Negl, Vol. 19, pp.1065-1075.

23 van Baar, A.L., Soepatmi, S., Gunning, W.B., Akkerhuis, G.W. (1994). 'Development after prenatal exposure to cocaine, heroin and methadone.' Acta Paediatr Suppl, Vol. 404, pp.40-46.

24 van Baar, A., de Graaf, B.M. (1994). 'Cognitive development at preschool age of infants of drug-dependent mothers.' Dev Med Child Neurol, Vol. 36, pp.1063-1075.

25 de Cubas, M.M., Field, T. (1993). 'Children of methadone dependent women: developmental outcomes.' Am J Orthopsychiatry, Vol. 63, pp.266-276.

26 Ornoy, A., Michailevskaya, V., Lukashov, I., Bar-Hamburger, R., Harel, S. (1996). 'The developmental outcome of children born to heroin-dependent mothers, raised at home or adopted.' Child Abuse Negl, Vol. 20, pp.385-396.

27 Bingol, N., Fuchs, M., Diaz, V., Stone, R.K., Gromisch, D.S. (1987). 'Teratogenicity of cocaine in humans.' J Pediatr, Vol. 110, pp.93-96.

28 Rahbar, F., Fomufod, A., White, D., Westney, L.S. (1993). 'Impact of intrauterine exposure to phencyclidine and cocaine in neonates.' J Natl Med Assoc, Vol. 85, pp.349-352.

29 Fulroth, R., Phillips, B., Durand, D.J. (1989). 'Perinatal outcome of infants exposed to cocaine and/or heroin in utero.' Am J Dis Child, Vol. 143, pp.905-910.

30 Hadeed, A.J., Siegel, S.R. (1989). 'Maternal cocaine use during pregnancy: effect on the newborn infant.' Pediatrics, Vol. 84, pp.205-210.

31 Calhoun, B.C.,Watson, P.T. (1991). 'The cost of maternal cocaine abuse: 1 Prenatal cost.' Obstet Gynecol, Vol. 78, pp.731-734.

32 Cohen, H., de Marinie, P., daSilva, M., Gelber, J., Laughani, S., Glass, L. (1988). 'Cranial sonography in infants of alkaloid cocaine (crack) abusing mothers.' Pediatr Res, 1095;34;4;2.

33 Flaherty, E.G., Patel, D.A. (1988). 'Urinary tract infection in cocaine abused neonates.' Ped Res, 1238;23;4;2.

34 King, T.A., Perlman, J.M., Laptook, A.R., Rollins, N., Jackson, G., Little, B. (1995). 'Neurologic manifestations of in utero cocaine exposure in near-term and term infants.' Pediatrics, Vol. 96, pp.259-264.

35 Konkol, R.J., Tikofsky, R.S., Wells, R., Hellman, R.S., Nemeth, P., Walsh, D.J., Heimler, R., Sty, J.R. (1994). 'Normal high resolution cerebral 99mTc HMPAO SPECT scans in symptomatic neonates exposed to cocaine.' J Child Neurol, Vol. 9, pp.278-283.

36 Zabaleta, I., Jhaveri, R.C., Rosenfeld, W., Sahdev, S., Vohra, K. (1995). 'Maternal use of cocaine, methadone, heroin and alcohol.' Neo Intens Care, Vol. 3, pp.40-43.

37 Chiriboga, C.A., Bateman, D.A., Brust, J.C., Hauser, W.A. (1993). 'Neurologic findings in neonates with intrauterine cocaine exposure.' Pediatr Neurol, Vol. 9, pp.115-119.

38 Lester, B.M., Corwin, M.J., Sepkoski, C., Seifer, R., Peucker, M., McLaughlin, S., Golub, H.L. (1991). 'Neurobehavioral syndromes in cocaine-exposed newborn infants.' Child Dev, Vol. 62, pp.694-705.

39 Chasnoff, I.J., Griffith, D.R., Freier, C. et al. (1992). 'Cocaine/polydrug use in pregnancy: two year follow-up.' Pediatrics, Vol. 89, pp.284-289.

40 Chasnoff, I.J., Griffith, D.R., Azuma, S. (1992). 'Intrauterine cocaine/polydrug exposure: three year outcome.' Pediatr Res, Vol. 31, p.9A.

41 Hurt, H., Malmud, E., Betancourt, L., Brodsky, N.L., Giannetta, J. (1997). 'A prospective evaluation of early language development in children with in utero cocaine exposure and in control subjects.' J Pediatr, Vol. 130, pp.310-312.

42 Laegreid, L., Hagberg, G., Lundberg, A. (1992). 'The effect of benzodiazepines on the fetus and the newborn.' Neuropediatrics, Vol. 23, pp.18-23.

43 Bergman, U., Rosa, F.W., Baum, C., Wiholm, B.E., Faich, G.A. (1992). 'Effects of exposure to benzodiazepines during fetal life.' Lancet, Vol. 340, pp.694-696.

44 Sutton, L.R., Hinderliter, S.A. (1990). 'Diazepam abuse in pregnant women on methadone maintenance: Implications for the neonate.' Clin Pediatr Phila, Vol. 29, pp.108-111.

45 Coles, C.D., Smith, I.E., Fernhoff, P.M., Falek, A. (1984). 'Neonatal ethanol withdrawal: characteristics in clinically normal nondysmorphic neonates.' J Pediatr, Vol. 105, pp.445-451.

46 Fried, P.A. (1989). 'Cigarettes and marijuana: are there measurable long-term neurobehavioural teratogenic effects?' Neurotoxicology, Vol. 10, pp.577-583.

47 Nathenson, G., Golden, G.S., Litt, I.F. (1971). 'Diazepam in neonatal narcotic withdrawal syndrome.' Pediatrics, Vol. 48, pp.523-527.

48 Kahn, E., Neumann, L.L., Polk, G.A. (1969). 'The course of heroin withdrawal syndrome in newborn infants treated with phenobarbitol or chlorpromazine.' J Pediatr, Vol. 75, pp.495-500.

49 Morrison, C.L., Siney, C. (1996). 'A survey of the management of neonatal opiate withdrawal in England and Wales.' Eur J Pediatr, Vol. 155, pp.323-326.

50 Oro, A.S., Dixon, S.D. (1988). 'Water bed care of narcotic exposed neonates: A useful adjunct to supportive care.' Am J Dis Child, Vol. 142, pp.186-188.

51 Theis, J.G.W., Selby, P., Ikizler, Y., Koren, G. (1997). 'Current management of the neonatal abstinence syndrome: A critical analysis of the evidence.' Biol Neonate, Vol. 71, pp.345-356.

Chapter 7

HEPATITIS B, PREGNANCY & THE DRUG USER

Peter Carey

Dr Peter Carey qualified at Liverpool University in
1970. He is a Fellow of the Royal College of
Physicians and has been a consultant in
Genitourinary Medicine in Liverpool for 20 years.
He has developed a specialist interest in HIV
medicine during the last 15 years. He has outpatient
and inpatient responsibilities in the Royal Liverpool
and Broadgreen University Hospitals NHS Trust
together with a contribution to community care.
He is an honorary lecturer at Liverpool University
and Clinical Director of the Department of
Genitourinary Medicine.

Hepatitis B virus (HBV) infection is present throughout the world and it has been estimated that there are 400-500 million people chronically infected: HBV carriers.[1] Instrumental in maintaining high prevalence in certain developing countries are mother to baby transmission, and horizontal transmission within families and between young people in schools. In many developed countries, HBV is mainly transmitted between adults. In the UK it has been estimated that 0.1 per cent of the population are HBV carriers. Drug users may be at risk of HBV infection if they inject drugs and share their injecting equipment. Drugs cost money and some users may have to work in the sex industry in order to pay for their drugs, or exchange sex for drugs, thus putting themselves at risk of contracting HBV and other sexually transmissible infections. A pregnant HBV infected drug user may transmit HBV to her baby.

The virus

HBV is an enveloped DNA virus with three major antigenic determinants:

- Hepatitis B surface antigen : HBsAg
- Hepatitis B core antigen : HBcAg
- Hepatitis B e antigen : HBeAg

HBsAg is found in the surface envelope whilst HBcAg and HBeAg are found in the viral core together with viral DNA and DNA polymerase required for viral replication within infected hepatocytes.

Infected individuals will have HBV in a variety of body fluids including blood, seminal fluid, vaginal fluid and saliva. The incubation period for hepatitis B is usually within three months of infection. Many infections are asymptomatic, particularly in children. Complete recovery characterises most acute infections. Fulminant HBV infection is rare and may be associated with HBV mutations lacking HBeAg.

A small proportion of infected adults fail to clear HBV, remain infected and become carriers. An HBV carrier is defined as someone who remains HBsAg positive for more than six months following infection. A proportion of these people will eventually develop chronic hepatitis, cirrhosis or hepatocellular carcinoma. Generally speaking HBV transmission may occur in one of four ways:

- Parenteral
- Sexual
- mother to baby
- Horizontal.

Screening of blood donors has dramatically reduced HBV infection associated with blood transfusion, although parenteral spread of HBV remains common amongst injecting drug users (IDUs) who share their injecting equipment. Parenteral infection of health care workers (HCWs), for instance as a result of needle-stick injury, is largely preventable as a result of HBV vaccination programmes, although a small proportion of vaccinees fail to respond. Proper attention to infection control and needle-stick injury policies and correct disposal of sharp instruments is mandatory!

Sexual transmission of HBV may occur as a result of vaginal or anal intercourse with an infected partner.

Horizontal transmission of HBV from an HBV carrier to family members may occur and is a likely method of transmission to children in countries with high endemicity for the virus. Uncertainty surrounds the mechanism for such transmissions, but it may be associated with accidental parenteral exposure to blood or saliva, or with mouth-to-mouth transmission.

mother to baby transmission

Acute HBV infection during the second half of pregnancy, particularly during the third trimester, may lead to intrauterine infection. HBV carrier mothers may infect their babies intrapartum, either from micro-transfusion of blood or from direct contact with HBV infected blood or mucus. Breastfeeding is not thought to be important in mother to baby transmission,[2] but it has been suggested that transmission may occur from HBV infected mothers who masticate their babies' food.

Diagnosis

During acute infection, HBsAg is usually the first serological marker to become positive, followed by HBeAg and then the antibodies: anti HBc IgM and anti HBc IgG to core antigen; anti HBe to e antigen; and anti HBs to surface antigen. In those who recover from infection, HBeAg disappears after several weeks associated with the appearance of anti HBe. HBsAg disappears later followed eventually by the appearance of anti HBs with the persistence of anti HBc IgG.

Chronic HBV infection is associated with the persistence of HBsAg (a proportion of individuals will also have HBeAg) and HBc IgG. The degree of altered liver function as shown by increased alanine aminotransferase (ALT) in the diagram below varies according to the severity of hepatitis (taken from 3).

Fig. 7.1: The chronology of infection with hepatitis B

The presence of HBeAg in the blood of an HBV carrier is associated with high infectivity, increasing the likelihood of HBV transmission irrespective of the mode of transmission. Loss of HBeAg with sero-conversion to anti HBe is associated with lower infectivity.

Maternal disease

HBV infection in adults is usually associated with clearing of virus and lifelong immunity but about 5-10 per cent become carriers. In our local maternity hospital most pregnant drug users with HBV infection are carriers.

The course of HBV infection in pregnancy is said to be no different to that in non-pregnant women. In those developing icteric disease, the period of jaundice is usually limited to about four weeks and may be presaged in the preceding week by a prodrome resembling serum sickness, due to the circulation of immune complexes. Urticaria, arthralgia or arthropathy may develop. The syndrome may be seen also in people without jaundice.

In most cases women can be managed at home unless complicating factors supervene (such as recurrent vomiting, anorexia or fulminant hepatitis). Periods of rest should be encouraged, with avoidance of prolonged or excessive physical activity. There are no specific dietary restrictions but individuals are advised against alcoholic drinks as they may exacerbate liver dysfunction. All unnecessary drugs should be stopped. Such advice given to drug users may lead to serious withdrawal symptoms if taken literally, and management should be coordinated with the drug liaison midwife and the local Drug Dependency Clinic with respect to continuing drug use, such as methadone maintenance.

The most serious complication of HBV infection in pregnancy is the development of fulminant hepatitis which may progress rapidly to hepatic failure and death in 70-95 per cent of patients. Bleeding problems may develop secondary to impaired production of coagulation factors, whilst respiratory distress syndrome or sepsis may be added complications.

There is no specific treatment for fulminant hepatitis other than intensive support, correction of coagulopathy and proper management of other complications such as sepsis. The risk of fulminant hepatitis is said to be less than two per cent.

Management by experienced specialists in the Intensive Care Unit provides the best environment for monitoring and intervention. Liver transplantation has been suggested for women in whom recovery from hepatitis is unlikely. No convincing data exist as to whether caesarean section, induction of labour or termination of pregnancy are of benefit to mother or fetus. For a more complete account of hepatitis B infection the reader should consult standard texts.

Effect of HBV on pregnancy outcome

Premature delivery (before gestational age of 37 weeks) is said to be two to three times more common in pregnant women with hepatitis, irrespective of the causal virus, compared with non-infected pregnant women and is most likely to occur associated with hepatitis in the third trimester.

Fulminant hepatitis in pregnancy leads to fetal death in about 70 per cent of cases but is not a feature of uncomplicated HBV infection.

Consequences for baby

Mothers with HBV infection who are HBeAg positive have about an 85 per cent chance of infecting their babies, compared with a 31 per cent chance if they are HBeAg negative.[4] Chronic HBV infection will develop in about 90 per cent of these babies, most of whom will have experienced asymptomatic infection although severe hepatitis will be seen in a small proportion.

Most babies who acquire HBV infection from their mothers do so during delivery and so serological tests for infection will be negative initially, seroconversion occurring during the first three months of life.

HBV infection persists for many years as shown by HBeAg and/or HBsAg positivity. Chronic active hepatitis or hepatocellular carcinoma may be long-term sequelae.

Prevention of mother to baby transmission

The Department of Health has advised that from April 2000 all pregnant women should be offered screening for hepatitis B surface antigen. In the UK hepatitis B immunisation is not included in recommended immunisation schedules. Methods to reduce the prevalence of HBV in the population such as screening blood donors, heat treating blood products, education about safer sex, specific advice to IDUs and their partners and the availability of syringe schemes will all help to reduce HBV infection in pregnant women, including the pregnant drug user. Identifying those at risk of HBV infection and immunising susceptible individuals is the strategy adopted in this country in the absence of routine immunisation of children or adolescents.

The vaccine contains HBsAg prepared from yeast cells using recombinant DNA techniques. 1ml of vaccine contains 20micrograms of HBsAg. Vaccine should be stored between 2° and 8°C. Freezing destroys the vaccine's potency. (Manufacturer's recommendations, Engerix B, SmithKline Beecham Pharmaceuticals.)

Immunisation stimulates the production of antibodies (anti HBs) against HBsAg and levels exceeding 100 IU/L are considered to be protective. Over 90 per cent of immunised individuals respond satisfactorily. Poor response to immunisation may be associated with HIV infection, other types of immunosuppression, presence of HLA B8 haplotype, age over 50, incorrect immunisation technique (e.g. injection of vaccine into the buttock), or inactivation of vaccine (see above).

Antibody levels should be checked about two months after completion of immunisation and if between 10-100 IU/L (poor responders) or less than 10 IU/L (non responders) a booster dose should be offered with further assessment of anti HBs. If response remains poor, reimmunisation should be considered. Double doses of vaccine may be required for some people, though such use is outside the product licence.

Protective antibody levels remain for variable periods of time in different individuals and may be predicted from initial response to immunisation.

Booster immunisation for good responders is recommended at between three and five years following initial immunisation, for those who require continuing protection against HBV infection.

Procedure

Active immunisation is commenced by the intramuscular injection of 1ml of hepatitis B vaccine into the deltoid muscle. This is repeated at one month and again at six months following the initial dose. Alternatively, an accelerated course may be used for more rapid immunisation. Following the initial dose of vaccine, repeat doses are given at one and two months followed by a booster at 12 months. This may be used for those requiring more rapid protection, such as travellers abroad or for those exposed parenterally or sexually to HBV, when this active immunisation is combined with passive immunisation with hepatitis B immunoglobulin (HBIG).

Immunisation is usually well tolerated. The most common side-effect is pain at the injection site, though fever, rash, malaise and flu-like symptoms have been reported.

The presence of severe febrile infection is considered to be a reason for postponing immunisation.

Susceptible pregnant drug users at risk of HBV infection should be offered active immunisation.

Passive immunisation with HBIG is available for susceptible people exposed parenterally or sexually to HBV. In the UK, small stocks of HBIG are held by the Public Health Laboratory Services who will also give advice about the procedure. 500 IU is given by intramuscular injection whilst commencing active immunisation at a different site. The accelerated course may be used. It is advisable to immunise within 48 hours of parenteral exposure and within 14 days following sexual exposure, the sooner the better.

Some mothers will be identified as having HBV infection during pregnancy. Protection of their infants involves passive immunisation with HBIG by intramuscular injection into the anterolateral aspect of the baby's thigh within 12 hours and certainly no later than 48 hours after birth. Ten micrograms of hepatitis B vaccine are given into the opposite thigh at the same time followed by repeat doses at one and six months. About 95 per cent of babies will be protected against HBV infection in this way. HBV serology should be assessed at 12 months of age. Further information with respect to active and passive immunisation against HBV infection may be found in the HMSO publication, Immunisation against Infectious Diseases.[5]

After delivery, mother and baby may remain together if their clinical status allows. Although HBV has been found in breastmilk there are no data to suggest that breastfeeding carries an increased risk of transmission and so breastfeeding is allowed if the mother wishes this. Proper infection control in the delivery suite should be observed and the mother advised about good hygiene and how to deal with lochia.

Whilst protection against HBV is well established, no immunisation schedule is available to protect against hepatitis C virus (HCV). This RNA virus is transmitted principally in blood, but sexual and mother to baby transmission have been described. Infection is usually inapparent but can lead to chronic liver disease in up to 50 per cent of patients. Diagnosis is made on the basis of finding antibodies to HCV, anti HCV IgG, in the serum of infected people. mother to baby spread seems to be associated with viraemia, detected by the presence of high titre HCV RNA using PCR.[6] Coinfection with HIV seems to be a risk factor for this route of transmission.[7] Blood/organ donors are routinely screened for HCV infection.

Hepatitis D virus (HDV or delta agent) is an incomplete RNA virus which becomes enveloped by HBsAg in order to establish infection (see diagram).[3] Characteristically transmitted in blood, sexual spread is also possible. Individuals may be coinfected with HBV and HDV, or HBV carriers may be superinfected with HDV. The latter situation may lead to severe hepatitis with progression to chronic liver disease. Serological tests for HDV are available.

Fig. 7.2: Diagrammatic representation of hepatitis B and D viruses

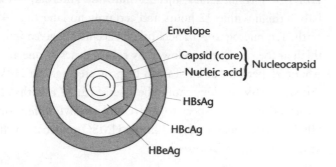

Hepatitis B virus. The envelope of the complete HB virion (Dane particle) is made of protein, lipid and carbohydrate components. HBsAg is located on the envelope surface and is a mosaic of three types of molecule: major, middle and large proteins. HBcAg is a major component of the core or capsid, which is a proteinaceous shell that encases the double-stranded DNA viral genome and polymerase. HBeAg is located on or within the core and is a cryptic antigen. It is secreted and shed from hepatocytes into the circulation when HBV undergoes active replication.

Hepatitis D virus. The envelope consists of a major HBsAg protein (95%), a middle protein (4%) and a large protein (1%). HDVAg and the single-stranded RNA genome are located inside the envelope. HDVAg is amorphous. HDV lacks a stable core structure.

Immunisation against HBV will protect against HDV infection, but HBV carriers cannot be immunised against HDV and thus remain at risk of infection from this virus and indeed HCV as well, if they continue risky practices such as sharing drug injecting equipment.

Individuals who have chronic HBV infection should be counselled about the possibility of other household members or sexual partner(s) being at risk from infection, and HBV screening should be offered to those willing to be tested. Those who are susceptible can be identified and offered HBV vaccination.

Conclusion

Much can be done to prevent the spread of HBV in the community. It is better to prevent HBV infection than to manage it in the pregnant drug user. Once identified however, mother to baby transmission can be prevented in most cases. Mothers with chronic HBV infection should be referred for specialist assessment following the completion of pregnancy. Some may benefit from therapy with interferon alpha, as may some with chronic HCV infection.

New antiviral agents are being researched in HBV infection, such as lamivudine and famciclovir, whilst interferon alpha in combination with ribavirin has shown benefit in HCV infection.

Users who continue to inject should be strongly advised about harm minimisation, in particular about the use of sterile equipment and not sharing injecting equipment with others. The topic is dealt with elsewhere in this book. This will protect against blood-borne viruses such as HBV, HCV, HDV and human immunodeficiency virus (HIV) and infections with bacteria or yeasts which may be introduced into the body by the use of unsterile equipment.

Safer sex practices (see Chapter 10, 'Sexually transmitted infections, pregnancy and the drug user') should also be discussed, particularly for users whose income for purchase of drugs relies on work in the sex industry or exchange of sexual favours for drugs.

References

1 Moradpour, D. and Wands, J.R. (1995). 'Understanding hepatitis B infection'. Editorial. N Engl J Med, Vol. 332, No. 16, pp.1092-93.

2 Vajro, P. and Fontanella, A. (1991). 'Breastfeeding and hepatitis B'. J Paediatr Gastroenterol Nutr Vol. 12, No. 1, p.141.

3 Teo, C.G. (1992). 'The virology and serology of hepatitis: an overview'. CDR Review, Vol. 2, No. 10, R109-14.

4 Beasley, R.P., Trepo, C., Stevens, C.E., Szmuness, W. (1977). 'The e antigen and vertical transmission of hepatitis B surface antigen'. Am J Epidemiol, Vol. 105, pp94-98.

5 HMSO (1996) Immunisation against Infectious Diseases. London: HMSO.

6 Alter, M.J. (1994). 'Transmission of hepatitis C virus - route, dose and titre'. Editorial. N. Eng J Med, Vol. 330, no 11, pp.784-86.

7 Zanetti, A.R., Tanzi, E., Paccagnini S. et al. (1995). 'Mother to infant transmission of hepatitis C virus'. Lancet, Vol. 345, No. 8945, pp.289-91.

Chapter 8

HUMAN IMMUNODEFICIENCY VIRUS, PREGNANCY & THE DRUG USER

Peter Carey

Dr Peter Carey qualified at Liverpool University in 1970. He is a Fellow of the Royal College of Physicians and has been a consultant in Genitourinary Medicine in Liverpool for 20 years. He has developed a specialist interest in HIV medicine during the last 15 years. He has outpatient and inpatient responsibilities in the Royal Liverpool and Broadgreen University Hospitals NHS Trust together with a contribution to community care. He is an honorary lecturer at Liverpool University and Clinical Director of the Department of Genitourinary Medicine.

Since the first descriptions of Acquired Immune Deficiency Syndrome (AIDS) in 1981, human immunodeficiency virus (HIV, the virus which causes AIDS) has become pandemic, affecting virtually all countries in the world.

UNAIDS/WHO estimate that there are approximately 33.4 million people living with HIV, over 95% in developing countries. During 1998 an estimated 16,000 people per day became infected with HIV.

HIV was discovered in 1983 and renamed HIV-1 in 1986, following the identification of an HIV variant (HIV-2) in West Africa. HIV-1 is the predominant virus throughout the world and several sub-types (A-J) have been identified. HIV-2 is less easily transmitted than HIV-1, either sexually or from mother to baby, and seems to produce slower disease progression.[1]

HIV is usually transmitted either sexually, via infected blood or blood products, or from mother to baby.

The epidemiology of HIV infection is complex, varying from country to country and within countries. Sexual transmission of HIV between men and women is the most commonly associated risk factor in many countries, whilst sex between men or sharing of drug injecting equipment are important in others.

HIV infection associated with the transfusion of blood or blood products has been reduced dramatically in most countries because of screening of blood donors and heat treatment of factor VIII. HIV transmission from transfused blood may still be a problem in those parts of the world where screening of all blood donors cannot be accomplished, and nosocomial transmission of HIV has been described from the reuse of needles and syringes.

In the absence of an effective vaccine or 'cure', recognition of the ways in which HIV is transmitted allows for the development of appropriate strategies to prevent the spread of the virus. Screening of blood/organ donors and heat treatment of factor VIII are now well-established ways of protecting recipients from infection. Education for sexually active people, (and indeed for people before they become sexually active) about safer sex and harm minimisation for IDUs, are similarly crucial in reducing the spread of HIV in communities. Programmes to control the spread of sexually transmitted infections (STIs) will, per se, control the sexual spread of HIV. Some STIs, for instance those causing genital ulcer disease, may be cofactors for the acquisition of HIV, further emphasising the importance of disease control.

The recent development of highly active antiretroviral therapy (HAART) has had a dramatic effect in reducing AIDS-defining illnesses and prolonging survival in people with HIV. The prescription of HAART in pregnancy will be discussed later.

HIV in pregnancy

The diagnosis of HIV infection in pregnancy causes much anxiety for women, their partners and their families, although some women who are aware of their HIV status choose to become pregnant. Many questions may be asked:

- What treatment is available?
- Should I continue with my pregnancy?
- What are the chances of my baby being infected?
- If my baby is infected will he or she develop AIDS?
- Will pregnancy make my HIV infection worse?
- Who will look after my baby if I die?
- Does my partner have HIV infection?
- Are any of my children infected?
- Who should I tell?

These and other questions demand time and consideration to answer. However, the significant changes in the management of HIV infection in pregnancy may lead to more women choosing to continue with their pregnancies rather than seeking termination. Counselling and long-term support will be required. The midwife would seem to be in an ideal position to give help, provided that she has the knowledge and skills.

For the pregnant drug user who has HIV infection, there is the added worry of the effect of her drug use on the fetus and pregnancy outcome. The remainder of this chapter attempts to deal with these problems.

Antenatal HIV testing

In April 1998 an Intercollegiate Working Party made some recommendations in a document – Reducing Mother-to-Child Transmission of HIV Infection in the United Kingdom. It recommended that HIV testing should be universally available, but that in areas of high prevalence (ie Greater London) it should be obligatory to offer and recommend HIV testing to all women receiving antenatal care. There is clear evidence that transmission of HIV from an infected mother to her child can be greatly reduced by interventions such as anti-retroviral treatment in pregnancy and in the perinatal period, elective caesarean section, and by the avoidance of breastfeeding. Some observational studies show that elective caesarean section reduces vertical transmission of HIV, particularly in association with zidovudine (see later).

Many centres now offer a same-day testing service where, following appropriate counselling, blood is drawn for an HIV test in the morning with a result available later in the afternoon. The timing of the test with respect to potential exposure is important, remembering that after HIV infection, seroconversion may take up to three months and occasionally longer. Positive results must be double checked against a further blood sample from the individual concerned. The necessary support services should be available to provide comprehensive assistance as and when required. This may require expertise from a specialist centre if not available within the maternity unit. Centres which regularly offer HIV testing include Drug Dependency Clinics, Genitourinary Medicine Departments, Infectious Diseases Units and Syringe Exchange Schemes.

HIV testing may be requested for other family members and should be undertaken with similar expedition and sensitivity, remembering that such testing remains a voluntary activity and individuals are not consenting to be tested for the doctor's benefit. HIV infection is not just a problem for the individual; it becomes a problem for the family as well if they are chosen to be involved; thus support should extend to those family members who require it.

The care of an HIV infected drug user during pregnancy demands the close cooperation of the obstetric team (obstetrician, midwife, drug liaison midwife), the local Drug Dependency Clinic or prescriber and the specialist in HIV medicine.

The monitoring of fetal development at appropriate intervals should be linked with close monitoring of drug use and education around harm minimisation. Regular medical supervision of HIV disease is also necessary with additional support from the counselling team.

The effect of pregnancy on HIV disease

During 'normal' pregnancy, CD4+ lymphocytes (T4 helper cells) decline to a nadir during the third trimester, recovering to pre-pregnancy levels at about term.[2] CD4+ lymphocyte function seems to be normal as does B cell function. Mildly depressed cell mediated immunity does occur, however, and may be associated with increased levels of circulating hormones. This may be associated with increased severity of certain infections in some women such as genital warts or malaria.

HIV infection in pregnancy seems to be associated with a more rapid fall in CD4+ lymphocytes, but without recovery to pre-pregnancy levels at term.[3] Furthermore, it has been suggested that the use of illicit drugs in pregnancy may be associated with CD4+ lymphocyte decline.

When the CD4+ lymphocyte count falls below 0.2×10^9/L (200/ml of blood), prophylaxis begins to prevent *Pneumocystis carinii* pneumonia (PCP), the leading cause of death in pregnancy in one prospective study. The need for this is now very much reduced due to HAART maintaining CD4+ lymphocyte counts above this level. The effect of pregnancy on HIV disease progression continues to be researched and remains controversial. A recent meta-analysis of seven studies suggested a possible association between pregnancy and HIV progression.[4]

Medical care

In 1994, publication of the ACTG 076 study showed the effect of zidovudine in reducing mother to baby transmission of HIV-1 infection. HIV infected mothers in the second or third trimesters were randomised to receive either zidovudine or placebo. Treated mothers were given intravenous zidovudine during labour and their babies were given zidovudine suspension during the first six weeks of life.

More than 400 mothers were studied. Vertical transmission was reduced by 67% in the treatment arm (25% transmission in the placebo arm, 8% in the treatment arm). This regime became the standard of care in many units caring for pregnant women living with HIV.

Subsequent to this, studies have shown the superior benefits of dual, and then triple, drug therapies, in reducing AIDS-defining illnesses and prolonging life in people with HIV infection. However there are little data on the use of such treatments in pregnant women with HIV infection.

Currently used antiretroviral drugs belong to one of three classes:

a nucleoside reverse transcriptase inhibitors (NRTIs) e.g. zidovudine, stavudine, lamivudine, didanosine.

b non-nucleoside reverse transcriptase inhibitors (NNRTIs) e.g. nevirapine, efavirenz.

c protease inhibitors (PIs) e.g. saquinavir, indinavir, ritonavir, nelfinavir.

NRTIs and NNRTIs affect the early part of HIV's replicative cycle whilst PIs affect the later stage. The combination of two NRTIs with one PI is referred to as HAART. Such combinations have a profound effect in reducing viral load (VL: a measure of replicating HIV in the body) to undetectable levels with an associated increase in CD4+ lymphocytes. Over time, this has been shown to prolong survival and reduce the incidence of AIDS-defining illnesses. The aim of treatment is to maintain an undetectable VL for as long as possible.

Combinations of two NRTIs with one NNRTI have also been used successfully.

Guidelines are available in the UK and USA for the management of HIV infection, based on symptomatic disease, CD4+ lymphocyte count and VL. They are updated regularly and include recommendations for the management of HIV infection in pregnancy and in babies or children.[5,6,7]

The effect of HAART on the fetus during the first trimester is unknown. Neither is it known whether there will be long term consequences for health for individuals exposed to HAART in utero. Women who become pregnant whilst taking HAART should be counselled about these issues. Some may elect to continue treatment whilst others may choose to discontinue HAART until after the first trimester.

Similarly, HIV infected pregnant women who are treatment naive but satisfy the criteria for commencing HAART, may wish to start in the first trimester or to defer until after this.

Ideally zidovudine should be part of the HAART regime, based on the ACTG 076 data. If this is not possible it should certainly be given to cover delivery, and be given to the new-born baby during the first 6 weeks.

For women not requiring HAART during pregnancy, the three part zidovudine regime (see British HIV Association guidelines) should be started during the third trimester. If delivery is by caesarean section, intravenous infusion of zidovudine should be commenced 1-4 hours before.

For HIV-infected women presenting in labour, who have received no antiretroviral therapy, intravenous zidovudine should be started as soon as possible and given to the baby during the first 6 weeks of life.

Babies born to HIV-infected mothers who have received no antiretroviral therapy during labour should be commenced on zidovudine syrup, preferably within 12-24 hours of delivery.

Women should be monitored carefully for drug toxicities and drug-drug interactions.

Regular health checks, often driven by the mother's own needs, are advised during the course of pregnancy, allowing for symptomatic review and clinical examinations. Visits tend to be more frequent in women with symptomatic disease. Most women will be offered a screen for STIs including syphilis, hepatitis B and also hepatitis C. New genital symptoms, genital symptoms in a sexual partner or casual unprotected sexual intercourse would be reasons for offering repeat tests and reinforcing advice about safer sexual practices.

Full blood count, liver and renal function tests, viral studies and urinalysis are included in the standard investigations, whilst CD4+ lymphocyte counts are monitored throughout pregnancy. Primary PCP prophylaxis is recommended when CD4+ lymphocytes fall below 200/ml; cotrimoxazole 960mg on alternate days being the treatment of choice.

Problems such as oral candidiasis and fungal infections of skin are usually easily managed with the prescription of topical anti-fungal agents but inpatient care in a specialist unit is required if opportunistic infections develop. For instance, PCP requires treatment with high dose intravenous cotrimoxazole, combined with corticosteroids, in the presence of respiratory failure, together with appropriate administration of oxygen. Secondary prophylaxis with cotrimoxazole follows acute treatment to prevent recurrence. It is hoped that such events will be rare with the wider use of HAART.

Other opportunistic infections should be managed appropriately, with the recognition that some commonly used drugs may have the potential for fetal damage. Fortunately Kaposi's sarcoma, an important AIDS-defining tumour, is uncommon in IDUs and in women.

Drug users who continue to inject during pregnancy may have problems related to these activities. Infection problems such as skin abscess, cellulitis, septicaemia, pneumonia or endocarditis, may occur. Tuberculosis is found more commonly in IDUs than in the population in general, and is a particular problem in New York City. It is less commonly found in IDUs in the UK. These issues are dealt with elsewhere in this book. The immunosuppression associated with HIV infection could exacerbate these complications and management in a specialist unit is mandatory.

Symptoms secondary to drug use may mimic those associated with HIV-related problems, for instance drug users withdrawing from benzodiazapines may experience seizures, as may HIV infected individuals who have cerebral toxoplasmosis or lymphoma. The caring team needs to be well aware of these problems. Two excellent reviews are referenced at the end of this chapter.[8,9] Issues around the prescription of antiretroviral therapy are dealt with later.

Effect of HIV on pregnancy and the fetus

Research from New York and Edinburgh suggested that women with HIV-associated pregnancies were no more likely than HIV negative controls to choose termination of pregnancy.

Data concerning the effect of HIV on pregnancy outcomes are conflicting. A study of pregnant IDUs with HIV infection in New York showed no association between HIV infection, spontaneous abortion, preterm delivery, still birth or low birth weight, compared with non-HIV infected IDUs. Other studies have confirmed these results. Conversely, African studies in non-IDU pregnancies note a variety of pregnancy complications such as preterm labour and low birth weight, but general agreement about the association of low birth weight and HIV infection. In these studies there is some suggestion that low birth weight may be related to the stage of maternal infection in pregnancy.

A recent meta-analysis of 31 studies investigating the association between maternal HIV infection and perinatal outcome showed an increased risk for infant death in developing countries.[10]

Congenital abnormalities do not seem to be found more commonly in HIV-related pregnancies and initial reports suggesting a specific dysmorphic syndrome have not been confirmed.

mother to baby transmission

Research has suggested that the fetus can be infected as early as the first or second trimester, but that intrapartum infection of the baby seems to be more likely (50-70%).

Primary infection during pregnancy may be a risk factor for some, because of the associated rapid viral replication and high viral load. Similarly, in symptomatic mothers with advancing disease the risk of HIV transmission seems to increase. This is usually associated with low CD4+ lymphocyte counts associated with high viral load. Lack of neutralising antibodies to HIV may also be a factor, whilst some HIV strains may be more able inherently to infect the fetus or baby. Certain STIs such as those associated with genital ulcers may also be risk factors for transmission as may be the presence of chorioamnionitis at term.

Mode of delivery is important in mother to baby transmission, with some studies showing considerable protection from elective caesarean section. Premature rupture of membranes and prolonged labour are likely to increase exposure to maternal virus.

Various studies show that the risk of mother to baby transmission of HIV ranges from 14 to 39 per cent, with the lowest estimate coming from the European Collaborative Study.[11]

Transmission during breastfeeding was first described in mothers postnatally infected with HIV. Estimates suggest that women postnatally infected with HIV have a 29 per cent chance of transmitting infection during breastfeeding. Subsequent research suggests an additional 14 per cent risk of transmission for mothers with established HIV infection who breastfed their babies following vaginal delivery.

Factors involving transmission as a result of breastfeeding have been studied and suggest that virally infected cells in breastmilk may be important while persistence of HIV IgM antibodies in breastmilk may be associated with decreased transmission. Substances that inhibit binding of HIV to CD4+ cells have also been found in breastmilk.

Prevention of transmission

Intrauterine HIV infection of the fetus may occur via the transplacental route, whilst infection during delivery may be consequent upon:

- Materno-fetal transfusion of HIV infected blood
- Direct exposure to HIV infected blood during delivery
- Exposure to HIV present in cervical mucus or vaginal fluid.

Data from the ACTG 076 study show the clear benefit of zidovudine in reducing vertical transmission of HIV. Mothers were minimally symptomatic with CD4+ lymphocyte counts greater than 200/ml. They had not taken zidovudine previously and seemed to tolerate it well.

Zidovudine crosses the placenta and has so far not been associated with fetal malformations, but babies in the zidovudine group had lower haemoglobins than those in the placebo group.

Work from the European Collaborative study suggested that caesarean section halved mother to baby transmission.

A study from the European Mode of Delivery Collaboration published recently confirmed the benefit of elective caesarean section in reducing vertical transmission in a group of women generally taking zidovudine according to the ACTG 076 regimen.[12]

The beneficial effects of zidovudine and elective caesarean section have also been shown in a study involving the French perinatal cohort. However, the same group failed to show significant benefit in reducing vertical transmission for caesarean section alone.[13]

In summary, the combination of zidovudine and elective caesarean section reduces vertical transmission significantly. Some specialists suggest that transmission rates of less than 2% are possible.[5] However, the effect of HAART alone, in reducing vertical transmissions, has not been evaluated fully and the indication for caesarean section continues to be debated.

Finally, vaginal cleansing with topical microbiocides in an effort to reduce neonatal exposure to maternal HIV has not proved to be successful, so far.

Whatever the mode of delivery, proper infection control procedures should be observed by maternity staff and following delivery mothers should be advised about good hygiene and how to deal with lochia.

HIV infected mothers are advised not to breastfeed their babies, bottle feeding with appropriate formula feeds being substituted.

Follow-up of mother: postpartum

Women who take zidovudine to reduce vertical transmission may discontinue intravenous zidovudine once the cord has been clamped. Otherwise HAART should be continued with close monitoring.

Advice about safer sex should be offered again, emphasising the success of condom use. The European Study Group showed no seroconversion for HIV amongst 124 couples using condoms consistently during 15,000 episodes of sexual intercourse.[15] Appropriate contraception should also be discussed.

If mother has symptomatic HIV disease she may require help with her baby at home and this may be arranged via her family doctor or through local support agencies.

Follow-up of baby

Historically the diagnosis of HIV infection in babies has demanded follow-up for a minimum of 18 months to allow for the disappearance of passively-transferred maternal antibody. Those with HIV seropositivity after this time are infected with HIV. In those babies not infected 50 per cent will be seronegative by ten months of life.

The development of polymerase chain reaction (PCR) for the detection of HIVDNA or RNA means that most HIV infected babies may be detected by age 1 month and virtually all by 6 months. A positive result should be confirmed as soon as possible.

Following completion of zidovudine suspension after 6 weeks treatment, babies should be started on PCP prophylaxis with cotrimoxazole until a diagnosis of HIV infection can be refuted.

It has been estimated by the European Collaborative Group that 23 per cent of infected babies develop AIDS within the first year of life with a death rate of ten per cent, 40 per cent of children develop AIDS within four years and that 75 per cent of HIV-infected children are alive aged five years.[16] The Italian HIV registry shows 70 per cent survival at six years and 50 per cent survival at nine years, for HIV infected children.[17] However, intervention with HAART should have a profound influence on HIV progression and on survival in babies and children.

The management of babies born to mothers with HIV infection is beyond the scope of this chapter but care should be undertaken where possible by a specialist unit skilled in the management of such problems. Usual vaccination schedules are followed with the substitution of killed polio vaccine for the live attenuated form.[18]

Considerable family support may be required if the baby has HIV infection. Such a diagnosis may remain, sadly, both stigmatising and isolating for many. The mother may feel guilty about 'infecting her child' and skilled counselling and support should be available for her. Careful supervision of drug use during this time is essential lest anxiety or depression from these events stimulate chaotic drug use.

References

1 O'Shaughnessy, M.V. and Schechter, M.T. 'Learning about HIV-2'. Lancet, Vol. 344, No. 8934, pp1380-81.

2 Tallon, D.F., Corcoran, D.J.D., O'Dwyer, E.M., Greally, J.F. (1984). 'Circulating lymphocyte subpopulations in pregnancy: a longitudinal study'. J of Immunol Vol. 132, No. 4, pp.1784-87.

3 Biggar, R.J.B., Paliwa, S., Minkoff, H., et al. (1989). 'Immunosupression in pregnant women infected with Human immunodeficiency virus'. Amer. J of Obs. and Gyn., Vol. 6, No. 5, pp.1239-44.

4 French, R., Brocklehurst, P. (1998). 'The effect of pregnancy on survival in women infected with HIV: a systematic review of the literature and meta-analysis.' Br. J Obstet. Gynaecol., Vol. 105 No 8, pp. 827-835.

5 Graham, P. Taylor, E. G., Lyall, H. Mercey, D. et al. British HIV Association guidelines for prescribing antiretroviral therapy in pregnancy (1998). Sexually Transmitted Infections 1999;75: 90-97.

6 U.S. Public Health Service Task force recommendations for Use of Antiretroviral Drugs During Preganancy for Maternal Health and Reduction of Perinatal Transmission of Human Immunodeficiency Virus Type 1 in the United States. MMWR: January 30, 1998; 47 (No.RR-2) 1-30.

7 Guidelines for the use of antiretroviral agents in pediatric HIV infection. MMWR: April 17, 1998; 47 (No.RR-4) 1-31.

8 Selwyn, P.A., O'Connor, P.G. (1992). 'Diagnosis and treatment of substance users with HIV infection'. Primary Care, Vol. 19, No. 1, pp.119-55.

9 Sherrard, J.S., Bingham, J.S., Owen, T.S. (1993). 'Clinical management of HIV disease in intravenous drug users'. Int J of STD and AIDS, Vol. 4, No. 5, pp.254-60.

10 Brocklehurst, P., French, R. (1998). 'The association between maternal HIV infection and perinatal outcome: A systematic review of the literature and meta-analysis.' Br. J Obstet. Gynaecol., Vol. 105, No. 8, pp.836-848.

11 Newell, M.L., Dunn, D., Peckham, C.S. (1992). 'Risk factors for mother to child transmission of HIV-1. The European Collaborative Study'. Lancet, Vol. 339, No. 8800, pp.1007-12.

12 The European Mode of Delivery Collaboration. Elective caesarean section versus vaginal delivery in prevention of HIV-1 transmission. The Lancet vol.353 no. 9158 pg 1035 – 1039.

13 Mandlebrot L, Le Chenadee J, Berrebi A. Perinatal HIV-1 transmission: Interaction between zidovudine prophylaxis and mode of delivery in the French perinatal cohort study. Journal of the American Medical Association vol. 280 (1) pg 55-60, 1999

14 Jeffrey S.A. Stringer, MD, Dwight J. Rouse, MD, Robert L Goldenberg, MD. Prephylactic Cesarean Delivery for the Prevention of Perinatal Human Immunodeficiency Virus Transmission: The Case for Restraint. Journal of the American Medical Association. May 26, 1999 – vol 281 no.20 pg 1946 – 1949.

15 De Vincenzi, I. for the European Study Group on heterosexual transmission of HIV (1994). 'A longitudinal study of Human immunodeficiency virus transmission by heterosexual partners'. N Eng J of Med., Vol. 331, No. 6, pp.341-46.

16 Newell, M.L. for the European Collaborative Study (1993). 'Natural history of vertically acquired HIV infection.' Paediatrics, Vol. 94, No. 6, pp.815-19.

17 Tovo, P.A., De Martino, M., Gabiano, C. et al. (1992). 'Prognostic factors and survival in children with perinatal HIV-1 infection'. Lancet, Vol. 339, No. 8804, pp.1249-53.

18 HMSO (1992). Immunisation against Infectious Diseases. London: HMSO.

Chapter 9

THE SEXUAL HEALTH NEEDS OF FEMALE DRUG USERS

Clive L. Morrison

Dr Clive L. Morrison is a vocational trained General Practitioner and has worked for four years in substance misuse and HIV prevention. In his role as Senior Clinical Medical Officer for Special Groups he provides family health care for drug users, prostitutes and HIV positive people. He has a unique expertise in the management of the complications of injecting drug misuse.

He has a special interest in the care and prescribing of methadone to pregnant drug users within the Liverpool Drug Dependency Clinic. Another role is to liaise between the local GUM and Drug Dependency services. He has collaborated in many research projects with allied health professionals, including the Regional Infectious Diseases Unit, with a particular emphasis on the health care needs of drug users.

Drug users as a group poorly utilise traditional health care services and female drug users in particular attend family planning clinics infrequently. Fewer than one in ten drug-using prostitutes in Liverpool had ever attended a Genito-Urinary Medicine (GUM) service in the previous 12 months.

This means that these women do not have accurate information on sexual health, contraception or sexually transmitted infections (STIs). Drug services tend to concentrate their HIV prevention strategy on the reduction of injection equipment sharing, although most HIV infection is acquired sexually. Changing sharing behaviour has been a lot easier to achieve, with the provision of Needle and Syringe Exchanges (NSE), than changing sexual risk behaviour in drug users through safer sex promotion.

Most female drug users are sexually active (84 per cent). Nearly a third will have an injecting, drug-using male partner. Although drug-using prostitutes usually claim to use safer sex techniques and condoms with their clients, less than a sixth will use condoms with their regular partner and only a quarter of all female drug users use any form of contraception.

There is much discussion in the research literature of the uninhibiting effects of drug use during sexual activity, and users being less likely to use safer sex and condoms. A significant proportion of prostitutes may use drugs while working, for a variety of reasons, but this is practically never a problem in the general population of female users.

Studies in the United States have made an association between drug use (especially cocaine) and STIs and syphilis. Over 58 per cent of prostitutes in Liverpool use cocaine and there has been no evidence of syphilis or other STIs in those screened in the Maryland Center. This is probably a reflection on the poor delivery of HIV and STI prevention services in the US, particularly via outreach.

Why drug-using women infrequently use condoms is difficult to assess. Over half of those using condoms are dissatisfied with their use. A quarter of opiate-dependent women experience amenorrhoea and they often believe that they cannot become pregnant. The levels of knowledge concerning fertility may be low, as sex education at school may not have been available to them. Some women may be in relationships where they are not empowered enough, or have insufficient negotiating skills, to encourage a dominant male partner to use condoms. Cultural and religious beliefs will also have an influence. Apart from prostitutes, female drug users have infrequent partner change and may perceive monogamous relationships as having no risk. If the traditional services fail the female drug user, then the onus is on drug workers to provide the advice and information that is required to reduce the risks associated with sexual behaviour. Unfortunately drug workers have not addressed these issues well enough recently – sexual health and drug misuse were fields apart until the advent of HIV.

Drugs and sexual health

The misuse of opiates can suppress the production of luteinising hormone and follicle-stimulating hormone from the pituitary gland. This disturbance in hormonal balance prevents menstruation but this does not necessarily prevent fertility or ovulation. Heavy opiate use may cause additional amenorrhoea by a different mechanism. Opiate use and a chaotic lifestyle suppress appetite with consequent nutritional deficiency. Associated with weight loss is the cessation of menstruation.

Women commencing methadone programmes have found that their periods return within a short period of time and they may become pregnant unexpectedly as they still think their fertility is suppressed. Contraceptive advice and/or prescriptions should be given to women when they commence such programmes.

Use of other drugs such as amphetamines, cocaine and the psychedelic drugs have not been shown to interfere with the female reproductive system. There is no interaction between any of the illicit drugs and the available forms of contraception which reduce their effectiveness, nor any research to suggest that the side effects are increased.

Some women have reported that whilst using stimulant drugs they do not produce sufficient vaginal lubrication during sexual intercourse and this may cause internal injury. It is recommended that they use a lubricant such as KY Jelly.

The contraceptives

Barrier methods

The HIV virus cannot pass through a condom. However, condom failure is reported and this is generally as a result of poor technique. Condoms can split during sexual intercourse or come off before the penis is withdrawn. Apart from abstinence the use of condoms is the only way to protect oneself from HIV and STI. The female condom (Femidom) offers more protection in that it covers some of the vulva and it also allows women to be more in control of their own contraception and protection. However, in the group of women to whom I offer contraceptive advice its use has proved to be unsatisfactory. The level of skill required for its use is high and many drug-using women find that it is not compatible with their lifestyle. Diaphragms and cervical caps are generally not advised for such women either, as although they prevent semen reaching the cervix, they give no protection to the vagina for the prevention of STIs. Their role in HIV prevention has not been determined but the presence of an STI significantly increases the risk of transmission of HIV.

Spermicides, often used in conjunction with barrier methods, have been shown to kill HIV but if they cause allergy and inflammation of the female genital tract they may, in fact, allow entry for viral infection.

Oral contraceptives

I feel that oral contraceptives may potentiate the transmission of HIV infection. Indeed chlamydia infection is increased in pill users. The pill causes columnar epithelial cells to grow onto the surface of the cervix (cervical ectropion). This vulnerable tissue provides a portal of infection and again can be exacerbated by co-existing infection.

Having to take a pill every day does not fit readily into the lives of some drug-using women. The mini-pill is even more problematic with the dose having to be taken at approximately the same time each day. Oestrogen-containing contraceptives have to be prescribed with caution in female drug users as oestrogens are contra-indicted if there is a history of previous cardiovascular disease. Due to injecting behaviour, some will have experienced previous deep vein thromboses (DVTs) and pulmonary embolisms and so will have an adverse medical history.

Intra-uterine contraceptive device (IUD)

IUDs increase the risk of HIV transmission threefold, because of menorrhagia and pelvic inflammatory disease associated with their use. I advise against the use of this form of contraception in female drug users.

Injectable contraceptives

Medroxydrogesterone acetate (Depo-Provera) is one of the most effective contraceptives, as shown in the table below. It only has to be administered every three months and fits into the lifestyles of most drug users easily. Drug agencies can even offer this service to coincide with their drug treatment counselling. Compliance is better than in those women on oral contraceptives who often run into difficulties due to missed pills.

Failure rates of contraceptives

Method	Failure rate per 100 woman years
Rhythm	16
Condom	4
IUD	3
Diaphragm	2
Mini-pill	1.2
Combined contraceptive pill	0.3
Depo-Provera injection	0.1
Female sterilisation	0.1
Male sterilisation	0.02

The disadvantages are that irregular periods are encountered when first commenced on the injection. Amenorrhoea may be caused by the progesterone, but is not usually considered a side effect in women who have been menstruating infrequently anyway. Once the injection has been administered any unwanted symptoms and contraceptive effect will persist for weeks until the drug has been cleared.

In a recent survey of over 200 female drug users in Liverpool, only two used more than one method of contraception. Due to the occasional failure of condoms, or forgetfulness, it is advised that these women use two methods of contraception; the first to reduce the risks of HIV and a hormonal contraceptive as a safety net to prevent conception.

Social and psychological factors obviously play a major role in which contraceptive method is chosen, or whether a method is used at all. Child rearing is a basic human instinct and the decision to become pregnant should be respected by the health care professional who may eventually have contact with a pregnant female user. Five per cent of female drug users are actively planning to become pregnant. Attempting to become pregnant carries with it considerable risks for a drug-using woman. A woman can only select a man to father her children from those that are available in her community. If that community has a high proportion of men who inject drugs and engage in high-risk sharing behaviour then this will be a risk to the women also. A woman will not have the opportunity to choose wisely a man who is likely to be infection-free. Before women consider pregnancy they should be made aware of the modes of transmission of HIV and given appropriate information so that they can make informed decisions concerning the risks that are involved. Preventing the heterosexual spread of HIV in this group of women will ultimately prevent the vertical transmission of HIV from mother to child which is now globally one of the major routes of transmission.

Pre-conception care

It would be best if a drug-using woman presented before she started planning pregnancy. This is in order that her health can be stabilised to carry her pregnancy through its term without any ill effects.

Some women may be underweight and nutritionally deficient due to chaotic lifestyles, appetite suppression by illicit drugs and poverty.

Dietary advice contrary to the 'normal healthy' diet of low calories and cholesterol has to be given in order to increase weight through meals containing high calories. Vitamin supplements such as multivitamins, thiamine and folic acid may need to be prescribed.

Instructing women to recognise the early signs of pregnancy and providing pregnancy testing will encourage early antenatal booking and access to midwifery and obstetric care. It will also be an opportunity to discuss the level of the woman's drug use and to ascertain whether she needs to be on an oral methadone-substitution programme. Many drug agencies will have priority admissions into outpatient treatment programmes. Commencing a methadone programme will help prevent women injecting and attempt to stabilize their drug use.

Pre-conception investigations in female drug users

Blood tests	Full blood count
Infection screening	Rubella
	HBsAg and Anti HBc
	Serological tests for syphilis
Genitourinary screening	Chlamydia
	High vaginal culture
	Cervical cytology

Blood tests will help detect nutritional anaemia and susceptibility to, and carriage of, infection. Some women in socially deprived areas may have missed the national rubella vaccination campaign for schoolgirls. Women should consider completing an accelerated hepatitis B vaccination scheme prior to conception. Discovery of hepatitis B carriage will be beneficial, as the neonate will be offered immunoglobulin prophylaxis for protection from infection in the perinatal period. HIV testing should not be offered routinely to drug-using women as this is often perceived as discriminatory and stigmatising. The majority of young female drug users who become pregnant have never injected and have had a monogamous relationship since coitarche, and so are not at a significantly higher risk than the general population. In areas with well developed HIV prevention services such as Liverpool, the HIV seroprevalence is extremely low and the costs incurred in routine HIV testing are not justified.

It would be advantageous for a woman to have a full sexual health screening in a GUM clinic. In a survey of female attendees at the Liverpool Drug Dependency Clinic, a fifth had previously had an abnormal smear test with nearly a third never having had a smear. This suggests that there is a significant risk in this population and that they require vigilant surveillance. Any treatment required or further investigation should be completed before pregnancy.

Some women who become pregnant may wish not to continue with it. Eight per cent of drug-using women who become pregnant eventually have a termination of pregnancy. They may feel their drug use is not sufficiently well controlled, or that their social circumstances have deteriorated to such an extent it is inappropriate for them to care for a child in such an environment.

Therefore, women should have access to abortion services. Even in some parts of Liverpool, discrimination exists as drug-using women do not have access to NHS abortion services. If the woman has the child it results in increased psychological costs of social service involvement, often requested by the women themselves, to provide statutory child care.

Sources

Donoghoe, M.C. 91992). 'Sex, HIV and the injecting drug user', British Journal of Addiction, Vol. 87, pp.405-16.

Hepburn, M. (1994). 'Preventing HIV infection in female injecting drug users', Maternal and Child Health, Vol. 19, pp.92-95.

Huws, R. (1989). 'Sexual problems and addiction', British Journal of Sexual Medicine, Vol. 16, pp.274-79.

Morrison, C.L., Ruben, S.M., Wakefield, D. (1994). 'Female street prostitution in Liverpool', AIDS, Vol. 8, pp.1194-95.

Morrison, C.L., McGee, A., Ruben, S.M. (1995). 'Alcohol and drug misuse in prostitutes', Addiction, Vol. 90, pp.292-93.

Morrison, C.L., Ruben, S.M., Beeching, N.J. (1995). 'Female sexual health problems in a drug dependency clinic', International Journal of STD and AIDS, Vol. 6, pp.201-203.

Morrison, C.L., Siney, C., Ruben, S.M., Worthington, M. (in press). 'Obstetric liaison in drug dependency', Addiction Research.

Morrison, C.L. (1993). 'Women, contraception and HIV', Drug and Therapeutics Bulletin, Vol. 31, pp.97-98.

Chapter 10

SEXUALLY TRANSMITTED INFECTIONS, PREGNANCY & THE DRUG USER

Peter Carey

Dr Peter Carey qualified at Liverpool University in
1970. He is a Fellow of the Royal College of
Physicians and has been a consultant in
Genitourinary Medicine in Liverpool for 20 years.
He has developed a specialist interest in HIV
medicine during the last 15 years. He has outpatient
and inpatient responsibilities in the Royal Liverpool
and Broadgreen University Hospitals NHS Trust
together with a contribution to community care.
He is an honorary lecturer at Liverpool University
and Clinical Director of the Department of
Genitourinary Medicine.

The sexually transmitted infections (STIs) are a group of contagious conditions whose principal mode of transmission is by intimate sexual activity involving the moist mucous membranes of the penis, vulva, vagina, cervix, anus, rectum, mouth and throat and their adjacent areas of skin. Departments of Genitourinary Medicine (GUM) throughout the UK continue to be pivotal in their diagnosis and treatment.

Some of the principles involved in the management of these infections include:

- accurate diagnosis
- effective treatment
- investigations to establish cure before resumption of sexual activity
- partner notification (contact tracing) to prevent further spread of infection in the community or reinfection of the index case
- counselling around safer sexual practices
- the exhibition of a confidential, friendly, well advertised and easily accessible environment for patient care.

Whilst a variety of microorganisms have the potential for sexual spread, I intend to concentrate on those outlined below. Standard treatments may have to be changed in pregnancy because of the potential for fetal damage and there may be poor compliance in drug users if treatment is prolonged.

Bacterial infections	*Syphilis*
	Gonorrhoea
	Chlamydial infection
	Organisms associated with bacterial vaginosis
	Group B streptococci
Viral infections	*Genital herpes*
	Genital warts
Protozoal infection	*Trichomoniasis*
Fungal infection	*Vaginal candidiasis*
Ectoparasites	*Scabies*
	Pubic lice

Infections associated with hepatitis B virus (HBV), hepatitis C virus (HCV) and human immunodeficiency virus (HIV) are dealt with in separate chapters.

Space does not allow for lengthy description of each infection and this chapter is not intended as a 'do-it-yourself' guide!

Altered cell mediated immunity in pregnancy may modify the course of certain STIs. Some STIs may be associated with spontaneous abortion, stillbirth, congenital abnormalities or perinatal infection, whilst ectopic pregnancy or infertility may be a consequence of previous salpingitis associated with gonococcal or chlamydial infections.

The pregnant drug user may be at special risk of STIs if she has to earn money in the sex industry or exchange sexual favours for drugs. The effect of certain drugs may influence her sexual behaviour or her partner's, if he uses drugs. If she continues to share injecting equipment she puts herself at potential risk of HBV, HCV or HIV infection. These and other health problems associated with sharing injecting equipment are dealt with elsewhere in this book.

Syphilis

Syphilis is caused by infection with *Treponema pallidum*. Following an incubation period of about three weeks (range 9-90 days) a painless indurated ulcer, the chancre, develops at the site of inoculation of the treponemes, usually on the vulva but sometimes on the cervix. Genital lesions are associated with the painless enlargement of superficial inguinal glands. Extra-genital chancres have been described on the lips, tongue, nipple and finger. Transmission is usually sexual or from mother to baby. Accidental infection is very rare.

This is the stage of primary syphilis. Without treatment the chancre slowly heals to be followed by secondary syphilis about two months later, due to the widespread dissemination of treponemes throughout the body. Characteristically a symmetrical, non-irritable maculopapular rash develops involving all body surfaces. Mucosal lesions (snail track ulcers) may be seen in the mouth whilst hypertrophic papules (condylomata lata) may develop at sites of the body liable to friction and maceration, e.g. genital area.

Other symptoms such as headache, fever and malaise are included in a range of protean manifestations. Without treatment this stage resolves, entering the stage of early latency which ends arbitrarily, two years after infection.

Thereafter late latency exists, which may continue unchanged for life or be terminated by the development of some form of tertiary syphilis: gummatous disease (benign tertiary syphilis), cardiovascular syphilis or neurosyphilis.

People are sexually infectious during the first two years or so after infection. Mothers who have untreated primary or secondary syphilis during pregnancy will infect their babies transplacentally or perinatally, depending on the timing of infection. Untreated, they remain able to infect their babies for several years thereafter with the risk reducing over time. Treatment of the mother during pregnancy allows for treatment of her fetus in utero, as penicillin crosses the placenta.

Consequences for pregnancy and baby

Overwhelming intrauterine infection leads to spontaneous abortion, stillbirth or the premature birth, or birth at term, of a very sick baby with clinical signs of early congenital syphilis.

Infection near term or peripartum may be associated with the development of signs of early congenital syphilis during the first few weeks of life or a baby who has latent infection but who may develop late congenital syphilis and associated stigmata, later in life.

Diagnosis

Treponemes may be found in serum collected from chancres. Serum from moist or eroded lesions in secondary syphilis and similar lesions from babies with early congenital syphilis may also yield treponemes.

Syphilis serology	RPR	:	Rapid Plasma Reagin Test
or	VDRL	:	Venereal Disease Research Laboratory Test
	TPHA	:	Treponema Pallidum Haemaglutination Assay
	FTA ABS	:	Fluorescent Treponemal Antibody Absorption Test

These tests are positive in people with treponemal infections and do not differentiate syphilis from non-venereal treponemal infections such as yaws. Their interpretation is best left to an expert, therefore, in people who have no clinical signs of syphilis and come from areas where non-venereal treponemal infections are endemic. The RPR or VDRL are non-treponemal tests. They may give false positive results in some people when TPHA and FTA ABS tests will be negative.

Increasing seropositivity is seen for RPR, TPHA and FTA ABS through the primary and secondary stages, reaching a maximum in the late secondary stage. Thereafter titres decline slowly over time, even without treatment.

Passively transferred maternal antibody from a treated mother to her baby leads to seropositivity which declines to negative during the first six months of life. Stable or increasing titres in the baby equate with infection, treatment for the baby and further investigation of the mother.

Treatment

Mothers are treated with a course of intramuscular procaine penicillin appropriate to the stage of syphilis. Resolution of clinical lesions and declining syphilis serology titres equate with good response to treatment.

Jarisch-Herxheimer reaction should be anticipated and explained to the mother. It is common on day 1 of treatment in early syphilis (but may occur in other stages) and is due to rapid killing of treponemes; fever, malaise and headache are characteristic. Uterine contractions, premature labour or reduced fetal movements may be associated. Mothers should report these immediately. It has been my custom to admit mothers for observation at the initiation of treatment.

Babies with early congenital syphilis are admitted to hospital for treatment with either intramuscular procaine penicillin or intravenous benzyl penicillin. Follow up after treatment is for two years.

A mother who has had an anaphylactic reaction with penicillin should be treated with erythromycin. As this antibiotic crosses the placenta poorly, her baby should be treated with a course of penicillin following delivery.

For lesser degrees of penicillin allergy a third generation cephalosporin may be substituted, although cross reactions between the two antibiotics have been reported. The partner and any other children should be investigated and treated if syphilis is found. Some specialists recommend penicillin desensitisation for women who have a history of penicillin allergy. This allows short-term tolerance to the recommended course of procaine penicillin.[1]

Gonorrhoea

Gonorrhoea is usually acquired sexually. The causative organisms, *Neiserria gonorrhoea* (gonococci) are delicate and have limited ability to remain viable outside the body. However, they can survive in purulent discharge on towels for some hours and so accidental mucosal infection is possible.

Gonococci infect mucosal surfaces because of their affinity for columnar epithelium, with resulting submucosal inflammation and marked neutrophil response. The urethra, para-urethral ducts, Bartholin's ducts, endocervical canal, rectum, pharynx or eyes may be affected sites. Infection may be asymptomatic in many women, though some may complain of dysuria or altered vaginal discharge, usually within ten days of infection. Rectal or pharyngeal infections may be silent whilst gonococcal conjunctivitis is painful and purulent.

Clinical examination may be unremarkable or show purulent exudate from the urethra, para-urethral ducts or Bartholin's ducts, or muco-purulent discharge from the endocervical canal, with erythema of cervical columnar epithelium. The rectum may show evidence of proctitis with erythema and mucopus. Evidence of pharyngitis or tonsillitis is usually lacking. Rectal infection may be associated with receptive anal sex, though it is more often due to contamination by vaginal discharge containing gonococci.

Pharyngeal infection occurs from oral penile contact. If eyes are infected, by contamination from infected fingers, for instance, purulent conjunctivitis with erythema and oedema will be in evidence.

Presumptive diagnosis is made on microscopy by finding gonococci as Gram negative intracellular diplococci on Gram stained smears taken from one or more of the above sites. Pharyngeal smears are not examined because other Neiserrian organisms here may confuse the picture.

Microscopy is about 60 per cent sensitive in diagnosing gonorrhoea in women and so swabs from these sites, including the pharynx, are inoculated onto selective media to be cultured in a warm, carbon dioxide enriched environment. Specific identification using monoclonal anti-bodies, and antibiotic sensitivities, follow successful culture.

Pregnancy complications

Gonococcal infection may be associated with:
- premature rupture of membranes
- chorioamnionitis
- premature delivery.

Pelvic inflammatory disease (PID), due to direct spread of gonococci from the endocervical canal to infect the uterine cavity and fallopian tubes, is rare in pregnancy. It may occur early, but presumably the hostile environment in endocervical mucus and the obliteration of the uterine cavity at the 16th week of pregnancy by the gestational sac, have protective effects. Untreated gonorrhoea may be associated with post-partum endometritis.

Disseminated gonococcal infection (DGI) associated with pustular skin lesions, arthralgia and then septic arthritis is thought to be more common in pregnancy.

Infection of baby

Intrapartum infection gives rise to gonococcal ophthalmia neonatorum in about 50 per cent of babies. Presentation is usually within 48 hours of birth as a purulent conjunctivitis with oedema of the eyelids. One or both eyes may be involved. Diagnosis is made by finding gonococci in Gram stained smears and from culture of ocular pus. A pharyngeal swab should also be taken for culture. A delay in diagnosis may lead to serious corneal involvement and possibly blindness. DGI is rare.

Management of the mother

Single dose treatments are satisfactory for uncomplicated gonococcal infection. Some strains of gonococci are penicillin resistant and this should be remembered when selecting an appropriate antibiotic. Regimes based on penicillins and probenecid, cephalosporins or spectinomycin are safe to use in pregnancy, when treatments based on ciprofloxacin are contraindicated. Some women may also be infected with chlamydia, to which these antibiotics have no efficacy. Erythromycin is a suitable addition to treatment in this circumstance.

Following treatment of the mother two negative tests of cure are required and her partner must be investigated and treated.

Complicated gonococcal infection during pregnancy should be managed in hospital with more prolonged antibiotic therapy appropriate to the complication. PID, DGI and gonococcal conjunctivitis all have serious implications for health.

Management of the baby

Treatment regimes vary but tend to be based on systemic cephalosporins. When one eye is infected the other should be protected with an eyepatch. The affected eye(s) should be irrigated with buffered saline every hour until the purulent discharge settles. Tests of cure follow treatment. DGI will require prolonged antibiotic treatment.

Chlamydial infection

Chlamydia trachomatis (chlamydia) is an intracellular bacterium with a predilection for infecting columnar epithelium. Submucosal inflammation and neutrophil response characterize infection. Chlamydia and gonococci infect similar sites of the body and infections may coexist. Chlamydial infection usually results from sexual or perinatal transmission.

For many women infection is asymptomatic though some may complain of dysuria or vaginal discharge. Urethral infection may be associated with sterile pyuria whilst cervical infection may produce mucopurulent cervicitis. Conversely both sites may be infected without clinical signs. In practice most women are diagnosed by the detection of chlamydial DNA by PCR (polymerase chain reaction) or LCR (ligase chain reaction) in swabs taken from urethra and endocervix.

Pregnancy complications

Chlamydial infection may be associated with:

- preterm premature rupture of membranes
- preterm delivery
- preterm labour
- low birthweight.

PID is uncommon in pregnancy. Chlamydial infection may be associated with reactive arthropathy or tenosynovitis, or Reiter's disease: the combination or urethritis or cervicitis, conjunctivitis or iritis, arthritis and mucocutaneous lesions. These complications are far less common in women than in men. Untreated chlamydial infection in pregnancy may be associated with postpartum endometritis.

Infection of baby

Intrapartum infection is associated with chlamydial ophthalmia neonatorum in about 40 per cent of babies, usually developing five days or more after delivery. Clinical signs in the eye(s) may be similar to gonococcal ophthalmia neonatorum but in some, infection may be minimal.

The oropharynx may be colonized, with possible infection of the middle ear or descending infection to produce pneumonitis. The latter may develop within six weeks of birth, presenting as a staccato cough with tachypnoea and interstitial shadowing on chest X-ray.

Management

Erythromycin is the antibiotic of choice for treating chlamydial infection in pregnancy. One week's treatment is prescribed for uncomplicated infection. The estolate preparation should be avoided because of its association with hepatotoxicity in pregnancy. Tests of cure follow, four weeks after completing treatment. The partner should be investigated and treated.

Erythromycin syrup for two weeks is effective treatment for both chlamydial ophthalmia neonatorum and chlamydial pneumonitis in the baby. Tests of cure are as above.

Bacterial vaginosis

Bacterial vaginosis (BV) is usually found in sexually active women though whether it should be regarded as a sexually transmitted disease remains controversial. The hydrogen peroxide producing lactobacilli in the vagina are replaced by a variety of microorganisms such as *Gardnerella vaginalis*, Bacteroides and Mobilunci species or *Mycoplasma hominis*. The mechanism for this is incompletely understood.

The characteristic complaint of offensive vaginal discharge, which often has a 'fishy' odour and is worse after sexual intercourse, is found in about 50 per cent of affected women. Clinical examination reveals a thin, white homogenous discharge presenting on the vulva, vaginal walls and cervix. As there is no associated inflammatory response, vulvitis, vaginitis and cervicitis are absent, though BV organisms may be associated with PID.

Diagnosis of BV is based on finding three out of the four following symptoms:
- characteristic vaginal discharge
- vaginal pH > 4.5
- fishy amine odour following application of ten per cent potassium hydroxide to vaginal discharge on a microscope slide
- clue cells: desquamated vaginal epithelial cells whose borders are obscured by large numbers of BV organisms as viewed microscopically.

Pregnancy complications

BV has been linked with:

- chorioamnionitis
- preterm rupture of membranes
- preterm delivery
- postpartum endometritis.

Management

Metronidazole is a recommended treatment in non-pregnant women and has been used for the treatment of BV in pregnancy.[2] Present guidelines from the USA recommend the following:

- Women with previous histories of premature deliveries should be screened for BV early in the second trimester.
- Those found to be positive should be treated, as this might reduce the risk of premature delivery.
- Women with no history of premature delivery should be treated for symptomatic BV.

Relapse after treatment may occur and research tends to suggest that epidemiological treatment of sexual partners will not prevent this.[3]

Group B streptococcus (GBS)

Vaginal colonization by GBS may occur in up to 25 per cent of pregnant women, with up to 75 per cent of neonates acquiring GBS from their mothers intrapartum. Of these, 0.5-1 per cent develop disseminated GBS disease with a mortality of 50 per cent.[4]

GBS may be grown from swabs taken from the urethra, vagina and rectum, and cultured from urine. Neonatal swabs are taken from ears, nose, pharynx rectum and umbilicus.

Pregnancy complications:
- Premature rupture of membranes
- Prolonged rupture of membranes
- Intrapartum fever
- Post-partum endometritis.

Management

Various strategies have been explored to prevent GBS infection in neonates. Immunisation of mothers against GBS infection is being researched whilst intrapartum treatment of GBS infected mothers with intravenous antibiotics has been shown to be effective in reducing GBS transmission to neonates.[5] Prophylactic antibiotic treatment of GBS exposed neonates has also been studied.

Treatment of the mother and her partner during pregnancy is ineffective because of subsequent recolonization of the vagina by GBS.

Genital herpes

Herpes simplex virus (HSV) infection of the genital tract results from sexual contact with an individual shedding virus from mucosa or skin. In many cases the source may be unaware of his or her infection. Accidental infection from HSV contaminated fomites seems to be rare as the virus survives for only a short time outside the body.

Historically HSV-1 has been associated with 'cold sores' on the lips (herpes labialis) and HSV-2 with genital infection, but HSV-1 has been found in genital infection and HSV-2 in oropharyngeal infection. The majority of genital infections are associated with HSV-2.

In the UK there have been increasing numbers of people presenting with genital herpes during the last decade. Research in the USA suggests that 75 per cent of people with antibodies to HSV-2, indicative of previous infection, have no antecedent history of symptomatic disease.

Primary infection establishes HSV in the mucous membranes or skin, followed by local replication. Herpes simplex virus is neurotropic, entering sensory nerve endings in the infected site and travelling along the nerve to the dorsal root ganglion. This mechanism establishes latency. Following recovery from primary infection, recurrences may occur due to reactivation of HSV in the ganglion. The virus travels along the sensory nerve to produce further infection of mucous membrane or skin. This may lead to clinical recurrence or symptomless virus shedding.

The mechanisms for establishing latency and recurrences are not clearly understood. 'Triggering' factors, such as fever, trauma, anxiety, sexual intercourse, menstruation or exposure to ultraviolet light, are thought to play a part in reactivation of the virus

The chance of recurrence during the first year from infection is thought to be 60 per cent for HSV-1 and 90 per cent for HSV-2.

Sites of infection:
- Vulva, urethra, vagina, cervix
- Perineum
- Oropharynx
- Perianal area, rectum
- Other sites: buttocks, finger, eyes.

Clinical presentation
Symptomatic primary infection with HSV-2 produces marked local and systemic symptoms which are less severe in those who have experienced previous infection with HSV-1. The incubation period is usually within seven days of infection. Following vulval irritation, vesicles develop which then ulcerate. The area involved may be extensive and involve the vulva and perianal area. Genital pain is characteristic, with marked dysuria, due either to urethral infection or to urine contact with genital ulcers. Superficial inguinal glands are likely to be enlarged and tender. Fever is common, with headache and myalgia. Aseptic meningitis complicates a proportion of cases. Rarely, autonomic dysfunction is encountered, presenting with urinary retention and a large atonic bladder. This should not be confused with the avoidance of micturition in women with severe genital herpes, particularly with urethral involvement, when it becomes too painful to pass urine.

Oropharyngeal infection may be associated with erythema or ulceration of the palate or pharynx with associated tender cervical lympha-denopathy.

Other non-genital sites of infection include the buttocks, finger or eye(s). Such lesions develop later and are probably the result of autoinoculation of HSV from genital lesions.

Healing takes place over two to three weeks with crusting of skin lesions and re-epithelialization of mucosal lesions. Secondary bacterial infection is uncommon but vaginal discharge may be prominent in the presence of herpetic cervicitis. The cervix is infected in up to 90 per cent of primary episodes: vaginal candidiasis may coexist.

Recurrences are less extensive or severe than primary episodes with resolution of lesions within seven to ten days. Recurrence rates vary between individuals.

Diagnosis

Swabs from herpetic lesions are sent in transport medium to the laboratory. Positive results from tissue culture are available within 48 to 72 hours. Direct electron microscopy for herpes virus in smears from lesions may be available in some laboratories. This investigation will not differentiate herpes simplex viruses from other herpes viruses such as *Varicella zoster* virus.

At present most laboratories are unable to detect antibodies specific for HSV-1 or HSV-2 and so individuals who are infected asymptomatically with these viruses cannot be differentiated. The *Herpes simplex* virus complement fixation test (HSCFT) is universally available but does not differentiate between HSV-1 and HSV-2. Its value is in the diagnosis of primary infection when seroconversion and rising titre will be seen.

Management

The principles involved should address:

- protecting women who have not previously experienced genital herpes from partners who have histories of either genital or orolabial herpes
- preventing peripartum HSV infection of neonates from mothers with histories of genital herpes, mothers with exposure to HSV during pregnancy or mothers with primary genital herpes particularly during the last trimester or at term
- preventing post-partum HSV infection of babies from parents or attendants with labial or orolabial herpes.

Detailed advice is beyond the scope of this chapter but may be outlined as follows.

Protecting the mother

Abstinence from sexual intercourse (rarely possible) or consistent condom use for HSV discordant couples to protect mother from acquiring infection during pregnancy.

Counselling about risks of HSV transmission from oral-genital contact for male partners with a history of labial or orolabial herpes.

Management during pregnancy

Aciclovir has been prescribed for pregnant women with symptomatic primary herpes genitalis during the first and second trimesters. Prophylactic aciclovir during the last four weeks of pregnancy may prevent recurrence at term obviating the need for caesarean section.

If primary infection occurs during the third trimester, particularly within six weeks of delivery, caesarean section should be considered because of the high risk of virus shedding during labour. Similar advice is given for primary infection at term. In either situation if caesarean section cannot be achieved and the decision is to deliver vaginally, intrapartum treatment with intravenous aciclovir, followed by postpartum treatment for both mother and baby, should be given. Caesarean section is recommended for women with recurrence of genital herpes at term.

Women at risk from HSV infection during pregnancy should be examined for genital herpes at ANC visits and swabs taken for confirmatory culture from suspicious lesions. If primary genital herpes develops during the third trimester or at term, the management procedures outlined above should be followed. Women with primary episodes before the third trimester may deliver vaginally if there is no recurrence at term.

Women with histories of genital herpes, virologically confirmed, should deliver vaginally unless herpetic lesions are present at term.

Despite these precautions, neonates will still be infected by mothers with no prior history of genital herpes who shed virus asymptomatically at term. This is likely to produce strong feelings of guilt in mothers who will require expert counselling.

Management of the baby

Babies born vaginally to mothers with genital herpes should have swabs taken for HSV from the eyes, oropharynx and areas of skin trauma. Note that trauma to the baby from instruments or scalp electrodes during delivery may increase the risk of neonatal HSV infection.

Treatment with intravenous aciclovir should be given to:
- babies with positive HSV cultures
- babies with clinical signs of HSV infection.

Prophylactic aciclovir should be given to babies born vaginally to mothers with primary genital herpes at term and may be considered for babies born vaginally to mothers with recurrences at term.

Prevention of postnatal infection

Parents, other family members or staff with orolabial infections should be counselled about the possible risk of HSV transmission to the baby. Mothers with HSV lesions on their breasts should not breastfeed.

Close liaison between the obstetric team, paediatrician and GUM physician is essential for the proper coordination of care.

Genital warts

The sexual transmission of human papilloma virus (HPV) may produce a disease spectrum ranging from sub-clinical genital tract infection to overt clinical disease characterized by genital warts. It is not known how frequently genital HPV infection is acquired non-sexually.

HPV DNA typing has demonstrated more than 100 genotypes. HPV 6 and 11 are most commonly associated with anogenital warts whilst HPV 16, 18 and 31 are associated with cervical intraepithelial neoplasia and invasive squamous cell carcinoma of the cervix.

Disease spectrum

1 Sub-clinical infection in the genital tract
2 Clinically obvious warts affecting vulva, vagina, cervix, perineum or anus

3 Cellular changes of HPV on cervical cytology

4 Vulval, vaginal or cervical intraepithelium neoplasia
   (VIN, VAIN, CIN)

5 Bowenoid papulosis

6 Oral warts.

The incubation period for the development of genital warts is up to six months, possibly more, following sexual acquisition of HPV. It is not known whether there is any difference in sexual infectivity between individuals who have warts in the genital tract compared with those subclinically infected with HPV.

At present it is not possible to eradicate HPV from the genital tract and so the aim of treatment is to remove visible warts.

HPV and pregnancy
HPV infection does not appear to have any adverse effect on pregnancy outcome, but genital warts may increase in size and number. In some instances the degree of HPV associated CIN has worsened.

HPV and the baby
There is an association between the development of juvenile laryngeal papillomata and the presence of HPV in the maternal genital tract at delivery. Infection is peripartum and uncommon. Peripartum HPV infection of the anogenital area of the baby may also be a rare occurrence. It should be remembered that the development of anogenital warts in a baby may be associated with sexual abuse.

Management
Genital warts are usually treated with podophyllin or podophyllotoxin preparations which are contraindicated in pregnancy. Treatment with the CO2 cryoprobe or liquid nitrogen may be effective as may the careful topical application of 90% trichloroacetic acid. This preparation should be used with great care as painful skin ulceration may be the result of overenthusiastic use. Irrespective of treatment choice, a small number of warts should be treated initially to assess response. It has been my practice to restrict the use of trichloroacetic acid to external warts only.

Biopsy is recommended if the diagnosis of genital warts is in doubt, and should be considered before the treatment of anogenital warts in babies if sexual abuse is a possibility.

The treatment of genital warts in babies requires the close cooperation of the mother and clinic staff. CO_2 cryotherapy is time-consuming and therefore difficult in practice. Careful electrodesiccation of warts, following local anaesthesia, may be useful.

Prevention

Caesarean section is not recommended to prevent HPV infection in the baby. However, it may be necessary if genital warts become so extensive as to obstruct labour or prevent episiotomy. This complication is fortunately rare. Biopsy may be required to exclude malignancy.

Regular condom use may be successful in preventing HPV acquisition for some men but HPV may infect the genital area which remains unprotected during sexual intercourse.

Trichomoniasis

Infection with the protozoon *Trichomonas vaginalis* (TV) may be associated with vulvitis, vaginitis and cervicitis.

Vulval pruritus, vaginal discharge and dysuria are the main complaints. A proportion of women have no associated symptoms.

TV infection is usually acquired sexually though non-sexually acquired infection has been reported. Diagnosis is made by finding the characteristically motile trichomonads on microscopy of a wet preparation of vaginal discharge in the presence of neutrophils. TV may be cultured from vaginal swabs inoculated into Feinberg Whittington medium.

Management

Metronidazole is the treatment of choice for TV infections. Some specialists are concerned about its use during the first trimester, and use clotrimazole vaginal cream, which has some anti-trichomonal activity, instead. Short-term high dose metronidazole regimens are not recommended by the manufacturers, for use in pregnancy.

In some people metronidazole has a disulfiram-like action when alcoholic beverages are drunk, and may produce headaches, flushing, nausea or vomiting. They should be warned not to drink alcohol when taking metronidazole.

Male partners, who may be asymptomatic, should be investigated and treated.

Pregnancy complications
Research data suggest that vaginal trichomoniasis may be associated with preterm delivery.

Intrapartum transmission to a female baby with vaginal colonization is said to be uncommon.

Vaginal candidiasis
Vulvo-vaginal candidiasis is seen commonly in women during their reproductive years, with about 20 per cent carrying Candida species in the genital tract. The majority of yeasts isolated from the vagina are *Candida albicans*. Factors predisposing to symptomatic disease include pregnancy, diabetes mellitus, antibiotic therapy and local factors such as close fitting nylon underwear. The bowel may be a source for recurring candidal infection in some women. Sexual transmission may also be a source of infection, though this is difficult to prove.

Vulval pruritis, with or without vaginal discharge, is the usual presentation. Vulvitis is obvious on clinical examination, with vaginal erythema and usually a white caseous discharge. In pregnancy symptoms are said to be more severe and episodes more frequent.

Diagnosis
Microscopic examination of a wet preparation of vaginal discharge may reveal the characteristic morphology of the yeast, whilst culture is the most sensitive diagnostic test. Testing urine for glucose should be routine.

Management
Candidiasis in pregnancy is seldom associated with complications, though cases of chorioamnionitis have been described. Frequent relapses warrant

investigation for predisposing causes, remembering that recurrent genital candidiasis may be a feature of HIV-1 infection in some women.

Topical treatments based on clotrimazole, miconazole or econazole creams are commonly used and effective. Systemic treatments with fluconazole and itraconazole are contraindicated in pregnancy. The partner should be treated if balanitis is present and consideration given to epidemiological treatment should recurrences of vulvovaginitis present.

Perinatal infection of the baby may be associated with oral or genital candidiasis. Nystatin suspension is suitable for oral infection, with topical treatment to the involved skin. Nystatin cream or clotrimazole cream may be used.

Scabies

Infection with *Sarcoptes scabiei* has no effect on pregnancy, fetus or baby and is acquired either sexually or from close body contact with an infected individual. Pruritus, worse at night, develops about one month after infection but much earlier in those who have been infected previously. Treatment is with topical application of permethrin 5% cream. The sexual partner and close family members should also be treated.

Pubic lice (*Pediculosis pubis*)

Infestation with *Phthirus pubis* (the 'crab louse') has no consequences for pregnancy, fetus or baby. Pubic, perianal, axillary and other coarse body hair may be involved. Rarely, eyebrows or eyelashes may be sites affected.

If infestation is sparse individual lice and eggs (nits) may be picked off. Heavier infestation may be treated with the topical application of permethrin 1% cream rinse. Occlusive ophthalmic ointment may be used to treat the eyelashes.

Traditional recommendations to launder recently used clothes and bedlinen apply in the management of both scabies and pubic lice.

Safer sex

If you don't have a sexual infection and your partner doesn't, sexual intercourse is 'safe', i.e. there is no infection within the relationship to transmit sexually. Many people don't possess these facts about themselves or their partners and for them safer sex means the use of condoms to protect against infection. Their consistent use before any genital contact is made should be emphasized. Following ejaculation the condom should be held firmly around the erect penis during withdrawal, to prevent leakage of semen.

Condoms are also recommended for oral-penile sex, with flavoured varieties available. Dental dams, thin squares of latex rubber (also flavoured) have been suggested for application to the vulva, prior to and during oral-vulval sex, so protecting two potential sites of infection.

Safer sex may not sound very romantic but neither is the acquisition of a sexually transmitted infection!

Further information about safer sex may be obtained from your local GUM Clinic (see below).

Conclusion

Regular screening of women at risk of STIs will help to reduce the prevalence of these conditions in pregnancy. The diagnosis of one STI necessitates investigations for others. GUM clinics are best equipped for this task.

Routine testing for syphilis should continue in antenatal clinics and should be repeated later in pregnancy, if new STIs are discovered.

Repeat screening for STIs in pregnancy should be considered for women who may be having unprotected sex with different partners. The consistent practice of safer sex will complement screening for STIs.

There is a comprehensive network of GUM clinics throughout the UK with enthusiastic medical staff, nursing staff and health advisers available to give advice in person, by telephone or to act as a source of referral for patients with a wide range of sexual health problems. A list of GUM clinics in the UK can be obtained by telephoning 0800 665544.

References

1 MMWR Guidelines pp.41, 46-48.

2 MMWR Guidelines pp.73-74.

3 McGregor, J.A., French, J.I., Milligan, K. et al (1994). 'Bacterial vaginosis is associated with prematurity and vaginal fluid mucinase and sialidase: Results of a controlled trial of topical clindamycin cream.' Am J Obstet Gynecol., Vol. 170, No. 4, pp.1048-58.

4 Adimora, A.A., Hamilton, H., Holmes, K.K., Sparling, P.F. (1994). Sexually Transmitted Diseases. Companion Handbook. Second Edition. USA: McGraw-Hill Inc.

5 Katz, V.L., Moos, M.K., Cefalo, R.C. et al (1994). 'Group B streptococci: Results of a protocol of antepartum screening and intrapartum treatment.' Am J Obstet Gynecol, Vol. 170, No. 2, pp. 521-26.

Chapter 11

OUTREACH WORK WITH FEMALE SEX WORKERS IN LIVERPOOL

Lyn Matthews

Lyn Matthews is a Drugs Counsellor at the
Merseyside Drugs Council in Southport and has
assisted in the development of services for young,
recreational drug users. More recently, she initiated
and assisted in the development of services for
pregnant substance misusers in the Southport and
Formby Health Districts. Until April 1992 she was an
outreach worker with Liverpool Health Authority.

The emergence of AIDS as the major health concern during the latter part of this century has forced us to reconsider a number of assumptions about the society we live in. Individual lifestyles, sexual practices and drug using behaviour have all been exposed in the light of a tragedy which continues to unfold. Moral concerns compete with a public health agenda which aims to prevent the spread of a virus which threatens us all. Despite this, common sense and compassion can often prevail, albeit for a limited period, in the most desperate of circumstances. The following describes part of my work with prostitutes in Liverpool between 1987 and 1992.

Background

In October 1986 the Mersey Regional Drugs Training and Information Centre initiated an injecting equipment exchange scheme in Liverpool as an attempt to prevent the spread of HIV through the sharing of needles and syringes by local drug users. At this time Merseyside, and in particular Liverpool, was being singled out in the media as an area of particularly high levels of heroin use, and the city was divided on how to tackle the problem. While local politicians played on community fears and called increasingly draconian measures to punish individual drug users, health workers took a more pragmatic stance, attempting to address the issue from a much broader public health perspective. Despite the very real threat posed by AIDS, giving needles to drug users was considered highly controversial and, in the words of one community activist, on a par with 'giving guns to murderers'. In hindsight, the 'radical' or 'controversial' nature of this approach, which has since been adopted worldwide, now seems exactly what it was to us at the time – common sense.

To avoid a media backlash and public over-reaction, the cooperation of the police and local newspaper were secured on the basis that this 'experiment', although in the best interests of society, may not even get off the ground. Injecting drug users are a marginalized and, consequently, highly suspicious group and to attract them into the scheme a user-friendly, non-judgmental approach was needed. To advertise the service, news of its location was spread by word of mouth in the first instance.

Although hampered by an almost covert operational policy and with minimal staffing, word of the initiative travelled quickly among drug users and the scheme began attracting clients from the city and outlying areas. In the first six weeks of operation over 300 people came in to exchange used needles and syringes.

As well as supplying clean injecting equipment, staff at the centre also provided free condoms and advice on safer sex. Among the women attending the scheme were a number of sex workers who also injected drugs. Initial discussions with these women revealed that sex workers operating in a particular area, near to the city centre, were experiencing difficulties in obtaining sufficient supplies of condoms for their needs. Consequently, it was decided to supply these women with enough condoms to last them a week or more, free of charge. However, these women told their non-injecting colleagues of the scheme and soon they too requested supplies of free condoms. The uptake of this service highlighted that although specific knowledge of HIV infection was scant, these women were sufficiently concerned by what they had gleaned from media reporting to take the issue seriously.

Initial work with the women led to the realization that a number of strategies needed to be adopted in order to develop a coherent approach to the prevention of HIV infection among this group. These included problem definition, information gathering, and the identification of specific practical policies.

The first step was to clarify the problem and define the target population. From informal discussions with the women using the syringe exchange scheme, it became clear that many of their clients were insisting on oral, vaginal, and anal sex without barrier protection. If a women refused to do 'business' without a condom, many of the men (or 'mushes' as they were called by the women) would drive on until they found a women who would. Given the fact that people engage in prostitution to make money, many women reported giving in to such requests. Also, the women's knowledge of HIV/AIDS and other infections, such as hepatitis B, was poor and in the main based on information gleaned from the mass media, much of which was confused, contradictory, or inaccurate.

It soon became apparent that immediate intervention was needed, and more detailed information was required in order to formulate and develop constructive prevention programmes. To this end, it was decided that condoms should be made more readily available and information concerning sexual health should be disseminated. It was also felt that contact should be made with more women working within the sex industry, although it was unclear how this goal could be achieved.

An early attempt to invite a group of women to a meeting to discuss AIDS prevention was a complete failure. No one attended. Traditionally, women working within the sex industry have received short shrift from straight society and are suspicious of statutory services of all kinds. One of the women explained why the meeting failed, 'We thought it would be full of social worker types' and, of course, she was quite right. Waiting to greet them at this meeting, alongside a neatly laid out cold buffet, were various dignitaries from the Regional Health Authority including the head of the Health Promotion Unit and his secretary, the Drugs and HIV Coordinator, the consultant psychiatrist and a social worker from the Drug Dependency Clinic, and the AIDS Education co-ordinator, amongst others. It was clear from this experience that, in order to gain the confidence of the women, entirely different methods were needed to reach this group.

In September 1987, I was asked by the Regional Drugs and AIDS co-ordinator of the Mersey Regional Health Authority (MRHA) to assist in a small exploratory survey of certain aspects of the sex industry in Merseyside. This request was initially rather intimidating. However, preliminary discussions indicated that there was professional support for the proposed venture from workers at the syringe exchange scheme, the genito-urinary medicine clinic, and welfare agencies. Accordingly, a pilot initiative was launched. It was thought that an informal 'outreach' approach would reach deeper into the hidden sector than conventional health or social work approaches. Outreach, as the name suggests, involves initiating friendly contacts with the target group on their terms, on the streets or other places where they meet.[1]

The main purpose of the project was to assess the knowledge and attitudes of female sex workers in relation to HIV/AIDS and other STI infections, and to design strategies for education and intervention into some of the more high-risk activities in which they might be involved. Field work was undertaken immediately, and contact established with the women involved. Although the women were understandably very suspicious at first, trust was established fairly quickly by befriending and demonstrating positive unconditional respect with regard to the women's activities. It was recognized from the outset that, if credibility was to be achieved amongst this group, a non-judgmental approach had to be adopted. To make radical changes to their lives the women needed to feel worthwhile and empowered. Starting from the perspective that what one does is 'bad', or that one's entire life is pathological, would doom the project to failure.[2]

As initial contacts developed, a clearer picture emerged of the size and nature of the prostitution scene in Liverpool. Although much of the prostitution scene in the city is difficult to explore (involving call girls, massage parlours, escort agencies, etc), it was possible to identify certain areas where high-profile street work takes place.

The scene

While an unknown number of women worked from nightclubs, hotels and saunas in the city centre, a sizable and very visible group worked 'the Block', a residential area on the southern periphery of the city centre. This area bears many of the characteristics of what ecological theorists call a 'zone of transition'; low cost, often run-down housing with a diverse group of residents that includes students and a high proportion of Liverpool's indigenous black population, and young urban professionals engaging in the gentrification of Georgian and Edwardian town-houses.[3] According to many elderly residents, this area has been used by prostitutes since the 1950s.

A hard core of fifty to sixty women regularly worked this area, supplemented by a peripheral, transient population who worked when they needed to. In the main, they would be in their late teens and early twenties, of low socioeconomic background and with a range of personal, social and behavioural problems. It appeared that levels of alcohol and illicit drug use were much higher amongst this group than could be expected of other women their age, which is not surprising given the kind of lifestyle they were involved in. The women worked street corners, with most of the clients picking them up in cars. However, during the frequent police purges on prostitution in the area, the women had to keep 'on the move' to avoid arrest. Although the women will always try to work in pairs, which provides both company and protection, this is not always possible, leaving them vulnerable to physical attack, abuse and robbery.

The business conducted by the women operating the dockland area in the north end of the city differs considerably from that on the Block. A hard core of thirty to forty women regularly worked the area, but this would vary depending on how busy the docks were. These women were generally older and longer established than those who worked the Block, and clients were contacted in clubs and bars around the dock locality. However, drug use on Merseyside has affected the sex industry considerably and over the past few years a younger group of women had begun to operate in this area also. Although Liverpool as a port has declined over the past twenty years, there is still regular trade with West Africa, the Far East, and South and North America. These women typically spend the evening drinking and dancing with the same client, before accompanying him back to the ship for the rest of the night.

The survey

Anecdotal information gave a very generalized picture of the scene. It soon became apparent that some hard evidence was required to support and direct any future initiatives. To this end, a simple anonymous questionnaire was designed by a researcher from Liverpool University. The survey was carried out during a three month period from September to November 1987, with 34 questionnaires being completed by prostitute women whose ages ranged from sixteen to thirty-nine. The results of the survey indicated that illicit drug use among the women was high, with 69 per cent reporting using illicit drugs, and the majority citing heroin as their drug of choice. More than half of the respondents did not know where to find an agency dealing with drug problems, and they perceived other health care services as judgmental and were, therefore, unwilling to use them. A large percentage of the women had been in care themselves as children, and many of their own children were also in the care of the local authority. Despite the insistence of many women that they almost always used condoms while 'doing business', the majority also had sexual partners outside work. Almost all stated that they never used a condom for sex with their husbands or other lovers.[3]

As a result of this exercise a number of objectives were defined, both short and long-term. The most obvious course of action was to make condoms and educational materials readily available and to encourage women who needed immediate help to attend appropriate services. It was also felt that, in the long term, a specific health response was needed, aimed at providing a more substantial service to this group, who were traditionally apprehensive of interference from health and social agencies.

The project quickly developed into a comprehensive service for the women and provided the first point of contact into services, such as the drug dependency clinics, GUM clinics and so on. One important priority of this work was contacting those women who were pregnant and using drugs, and accessing them into services. Many were reluctant to disclose their pregnancies, for fear of judgmental attitudes or losing their children to social services care. However, it was felt important that these women should be encouraged to take up the vital health care needed, for both themselves and for their unborn children.

Meeting Irene

My first encounter with a pregnant woman was on a cold and rainy Monday night in 1987. I had not been working on the project very long when I met Irene, a small blonde in her early twenties. She was standing with a group of women around a telephone box, which was a regular 'pitch' for many of the women who worked the area. She was heavily pregnant and working to buy heroin for herself and for her partner. As we stood and talked in the rain, she began to cry and told me that she had already had three children taken into care. She felt no one wanted to help her because she was a drug user and a prostitute. Before I left her she said to me, 'There must be a better life than this'. I was to learn some months later that Irene's baby was placed in the care of the local authority shortly after being born. This left me feeling very sad and frustrated. My own short experience of working with the women had shown me how marginalized they were in society. I felt that more could be done to support women like Irene, and that there was a definite need for development in service provision in this area of the work.

Irene became a regular contact of mine. She drifted in and out of prostitution, often spending short periods in jail. One night, about two years later, she told me she was expecting again. Although she was about five months pregnant, she had not yet seen a doctor or received any antenatal care. With my encouragement, and reassurance that every effort would be made to help her keep the baby, she agreed to be referred into the local drug dependency clinic and was prescribed a maintenance course of methadone.

At this time, the clinic had begun to prioritize pregnant women, recognizing the need for this special group to be in touch with services and also reducing the risks of HIV infection. A pregnant drug user would be taken into treatment straight away, avoiding the long waiting list the clinic had had to impose. The social worker, and other staff members at the clinic, were able to provide practical support for Irene following the birth of her baby. By clinic staff advocating on her behalf, Social Services recognized that not only did the baby need care, but Irene did too. Fortunately, a foster family was available which was willing to take them both. When the baby was born, Irene went to live with the family who were not only able to offer support and monitor her progress, but also taught her valuable parenting skills. This enabled Irene, for the first time, to care for her child. After a short period with the foster family, and a lot of hard work from Irene, she was able to move into a home of her own.

Receiving a regular daily prescription of methadone, Irene no longer had to work the streets for drug money and was able to rebuild her life. To my knowledge, Irene still cares for her child and has remained fairly stable. However, without that first contact, Irene may not have found a 'better life'. There were many more women who were referred into the Drug Dependency Clinic during my time with the project. This work contributed to an increase in the numbers of women using the service of Liverpool Drug Dependency Clinic by over 30 per cent.[4]

However, entering into treatment did not always prevent the women from working, as a prescription of methadone did not always stop them from continuing to prostitute themselves. If a drug injector was prescribed methadone linctus, which is taken orally, they would still continue to buy heroin to inject. Also, some women would find being 'scripted' freed up money to buy other drugs, such as crack. It must be remembered that treating an addiction to, say, heroin, does not negate the desire to get high on other drugs. They still drank, they still smoked cigarettes, and the use of a range of drugs is a normal part of everyday life for many of the women. Consequently, the script would become a 'flexible friend' to many, who used it in exchange for other drugs or money.

This also applied to those women who were working while pregnant. Many women would continue to work right up to the last minute before the birth. Some would even reappear on the streets only a few days after giving birth. As one women put it, 'I still need money, I can't keep borrowing all the time and the social [welfare benefit] is just not enough to live on. I know I've got my medicine [methadone], but where's the money coming from for all the things I need for the baby?'.

Changing drug use patterns

In the latter part of 1988 there was a dramatic change in the drug-using behaviour of many of the women I encountered. A fall in the purity and availability of street heroin led to many users switching from smoking to injecting, adding further importance to the use of clean equipment, condoms, and knowledge of HIV transmission. Furthermore, the availability and rapid uptake of crack changed not only their drug use, but also their work practices. Smoking cocaine produces an immediate, intense high that can lead to extremely compulsive and obsessive behaviour. Consequently, many of the women began working longer hours and engaged in more high-risk sexual activity to get the money to buy crack. A major concern was women who used crack during pregnancy, because of the damaging effect the drug could have on the fetus. Cocaine use during pregnancy has been associated with increased rates of placental abruption and still births. In utero strokes have also been reported in some of the literature available from America.[5]

The women who used crack during their pregnancies would report the baby 'stiffening up' in the womb when they smoked a 'rock'. One woman, who was expecting her second child and had used crack for several years, told me, 'The baby definitely feels it when I have a rock – and I can tell it doesn't like it'. All the women who smoked crack during their pregnancies felt guilty about their drug use, but appeared to be unable to control it. 'I know I shouldn't be doing it [crack] but it's hard, it's so hard'.

To further complicate matters, crack users often self-medicate with depressants, typically heroin or temazepam (a benzodiazepine), to cushion the extremely unpleasant come down. As the pleasurable effects of crack last only a few minutes, the user is left wanting more of the drug or needs to arrest the unpleasant after-effects such as paranoia and anxiety. One woman explained to me, 'I need a hit [of heroin] when I've had a rock. You just feel so fast, everything is racing, you need the brown [heroin] to feel normal again. It's mad'. Another commented, 'When you're wired, you just want it to stop. It's too fast, you can't think straight. A hit brings you right down'. Some of the women also injected temazepam, which led to serious complications such as deep vein thrombosis and abscesses. This form of abuse caused one woman to lose her leg shortly after I left the project. Poly-drug use at this level led many of the women, whose primary drug was crack, to become dependent on heroin.

The babies born to mothers addicted to crack tended to be smaller and were sometimes premature, but did not exhibit the severe problems associated with the American 'crack-babies' we'd read about in the papers. This may have been due to lower levels of use, easier access to health services, or less deprived conditions. In America, cocaine is far cheaper than in Britain; a vial of crack can be bought for only a few dollars. Cocaine still remains relatively expensive in this country, although users report that prices are falling and quality increasing. However, should levels of cocaine use continue to rise in this country, a different picture may start to emerge regarding the cocaine-exposed newborn.

Although most of this work took place on the streets, it was also important to gain access to places like 'shooting galleries' and 'crack houses', where drug users would gather to inject heroin or smoke cocaine. Work in this environment was extremely important, as injection practices could be observed, on the spot advice given and clean injecting equipment provided. This also allowed me valuable insight into drug using behaviours and trends, thus enabling the information to be used for further development of drug and HIV services. Although I felt privileged to be allowed into this inner sanctum of drug use, work in this setting is demanding and very stressful and it is easy to feel isolated. To colleagues, particularly managers, this is a totally alien world which they have difficulty understanding. By its absence I learned the value of supervision and support.

Despite what must seem a depressing and disheartening job, working on the project was both enjoyable and rewarding. Practical interventions with the women not only prevented the spread of HIV infection, but also saved many lives. Dina was an example of this. Dina was a small, black woman in her middle twenties who had turned to prostitution to finance her heroin and crack use. Her drug use began to escalate when her children were taken into the care of the local authority, and she began to inject temazepam into her groin. One night, in August 1989, I saw Dina limping down the road. Her leg was very swollen and I suspected she had a deep vein thrombosis. I insisted that she should go to hospital, but Dina argued that she had to continue working. After much persuasion she finally agreed, and she was admitted to hospital with a DVT in her leg. The doctor told her that had her condition been left another day, she would have at least lost her leg – if not her life. During Dina's stay in hospital, she talked about coming off drugs, so I arranged for her to go straight to a detox unit following her discharge from hospital. She then went on to a residential rehabilitation programme away from Merseyside, which she successfully completed. Recently, Dina and I spoke for the first time in four years. She now works at the rehab and is helping others with their drug problems. For Dina, the help, encouragement and under-standing that was on offer made a big difference to her life. She told me, 'Having someone who was there all the time, who understood and didn't judge me, made all the difference. But most of all, having someone who cared. I would not have done this on my own, not without the support I got, I probably would be dead now'.

My work taught me that these are invisible women. They may be ignored, pitied, or whispered about, but for most part they are unknown to us, hidden from our sight, suffering silently and profoundly. When the light finally shone upon this dark side of society's primitive and cruel treatment, I saw that these women were our mothers, our sisters, our daughters.

Epilogue

Over the last ten years there has been a growth in agencies providing outreach services targeting prostitutes and drug users. Outreach work, if performed effectively, is an important strand in service provision for this client group. Outreach workers can, by utilising simple interventions regarding health ad social issues – particularly in the case of pregnancy - make an enormous difference to the lives of the people they serve. Early interventions can and do save lives and result in more positive outcomes for the individuals concerned.

For example, I recently met a woman who had been one of my first contacts when I began working on the project. When we first met she had already severely damaged her body as a result of her IV drug use, which was extremely chaotic at that time. This woman had come a long way since my first encounter with her on the streets in 1987. Although she had not stopped buying drugs, she no longer had to work the streets to raise money to buy them, was able to exert a greater degree of control over her drug use and her health and lifestyle had improved beyond recognition. According to her this had all come about as a direct result of the intervention and impact the outreach service had on her life. For those who remain hidden and not in touch with services the outcomes can be very different.

In contrast, a black woman who had been addicted to crack for over ten years, recently gave birth to her child whilst remanded in prison. She also had two other children who were in the care of her extended family. The rest of her immediate family were either dead or in custody themselves. Although having used drugs and worked as a prostitute for all those years, she had had little or no contact or support from the services in her area. Prior to her arrest, she had been spending £200 to £300 a day on crack cocaine and was 15 weeks pregnant when she was remanded in custody. Having spent the remaining six months of her pregnancy whilst on remand, she stayed drug free and delivered her child and was accepted at a prison with a mother and baby unit.

When she was finally convicted, having pleaded guilty to the charges, she received a very lengthy prison sentence. In court, she had no one to advocate on her behalf or support her and there were no social enquiry reports undertaken. She now faces the prospect of having to give up her baby when it is 18 months old, whilst she serves the remainder of her prison sentence. Following her conviction she was to say, 'All I've ever got is jail, jail, jail. No one has ever given me a chance.' Maybe, if she had received appropriate support earlier, the outcome might have been very different. This case also highlighted the need for drug services to make more effort in the development of service provision for black and visible minority groups.

The use of drugs has continued to grow within our communities, with new health and social risks to those who inject drugs and engage in unprotected sexual activity. We can not afford to be complacent in our endeavours to 'reach' the hidden sectors of drug users in our society just because we have not seen the HIV explosion America has experienced. The emergence of Hepatitis C brings a new emphasis on targeting those considered to be involved in 'high risk' activities. In Merseyside, a high percentage of IDUs are already infected with this virus, despite years of preventative work being done with this group. This reinforces the fact that, in order to contain the spread of all blood-borne viruses, we must strengthen attempts to engage with this group if we are to encourage changes in behaviour amongst those most at risk.

However, health care professionals must also be clear in the messages they give to drug users regarding injecting and sexual practices. Building-based workers can often be unaware of drug using behaviours and rituals, which is where outreach work can continue to play an important role by providing information to static services. Despite (or maybe because of) the emphasis placed on syringe and needle sharing over the past decade, many injecting drug users continue to be at risk of viral infection through the sharing of drug paraphernalia such as spoons, filters, water and water containers.

Outreach work is often difficult and dangerous – particularly amongst crack users – requiring a high level of insight into the client groups' lifestyle and a great deal of trust between client and worker. The advent of 'gun law' onto the streets of Britain brings even greater risks to those undertaking outreach work and lends more impetus to appointing the right workers. Therefore, the selection of appropriate individuals is vital if this work is to have any impact. Outreach work has been 'professionalised' since those early days in as much as appointees now often require a qualification in nursing or social work. While qualifications may be important, the personality of the worker is integral to the success of this kind of work if they are to be accepted into the drug users' world.

This chapter is dedicated to the memory of Linda Donaldson, who was murdered in October 1988.

References

1 Matthews, L. (1989). 'Outreach work with female prostitutes in Liverpool'. In Plant, M. (Ed.) Aids, Drugs and Prostitution. Tavistock/Routledge.

2 Springer, E. (1991). 'Effective AIDS prevention with drug users; the harm reduction model'. In Counselling Chemically Dependent People With HIV Illness. Haworth Press.

3 McDermott, P. et al. (1988). Prostitutes, Drugs and HIV Infection. Mersey Regional Health Authority.

4 Ruben, S. (1990). 'The implications for drug dependency units'. In: Henderson, S. (Ed.)Women HIV Drugs. London: ISDD.

5 Kaiser, M. (1990). 'Cocaine exposed newborns'. Paedriatric Review. New Orleans: Children's Hospital.

Further Reading

Adimora, A., Hamilton, H., Holmes, K.K., Sparling, P.F. (1994). Sexually Transmitted Diseases. 2nd edition. Companion Handbook. USA: McGraw-Hill.

AIDS (1994) 'A Year in Review'. Current Science.

Ashton, J. et al. (1989). The New Public Health. Liverpool: Liverpool University Press.

Carmen, A. (1985). Working Women. Harper and Row.

Corcoran, G.D., Ridgway, G.L. (1994). 'Antibiotic chemotherapy of bacterial sexually transmitted diseases in adults: a review.' Int. J. of STD and AIDS, 5, pp.165-71.

Gleicher, N. (1994). Principles and Practice of Medical Therapy in Pregnancy. 2nd edition. Appleton and Lage.

Matthews, L. (1993). 'Outreach on the front line'. Druglink. ISDD. Vol. 8 Issue 2.

Sande, M.A. and Volberding, P.A. (1994) The Medical Management of AIDS. Philadelphia: W.B. Saunders.

Sherlock, S. and Dooley, J. Diseases of the Liver and Biliary System. Ninth Edition. Oxford: Blackwell Scientific Publications.

Chapter 12

DRUGS COUNSELLING & THE PREGNANT ADDICT

Neil Lloyd-Knapman

Neil Lloyd-Knapman BA Dip Couns has counselled drug users for over 12 years in residential, clinical and counselling services. He currently works at the Liverpool Counselling Service of the Merseyside Drugs Council. The MDC has operated a counselling service in the heart of Liverpool since the mid-1960s. The agency attempts to address the changing needs and problems created through substance misuse. Experienced counsellors work with both users and family members, helping them develop strategies to overcome the worst effects of addiction. A priority is to access drug users into primary care and establish contact with other helping agencies. In turn a referral for counselling and support can be made from any individual or organization.

In much of our society, the regular taking of illegal drugs is still considered a taboo. It is equated with weakness of character, illness and death. Users are at best judged as pathetic and at worst as evil and destructive. Practices such as injecting drugs are viewed as a threat to establishment values, they are vilified by the media and result in the marginalization of those that indulge in them.

The effect of this stigmatization can often push an individual further into the drug sub-culture, widening the gap between themselves and the 'establishment' world. Thus an addict will find him/herself on the edge of criminality by the nature of his/her addiction. With a growing tolerance to a relatively expensive commodity, few means to support it and other users at hand to lead the way it is small wonder that many will become firmly enmeshed in a criminal lifestyle, and increasingly marginalized from mainstream society.

When a drug-using woman becomes pregnant and, for health, social and perhaps economic reasons, requires the services that are available for all women, she may avoid or decline them. Fear can be a major factor, not simply for herself or the child, but as a result of stigmatization. This is a fear of being judged negatively, as a drug user, as a woman and as a mother.

For many women addicted to drugs, the arrival of a baby can prove to be a turning point in their lives. It can be a focus for a new strength and acceptance of unique responsibilities. As such it can mean either a passage back to mainstream living or another event in which they fail and fall further behind.

Family support

Many women expecting their first child can expect a great deal of support from parents and extended family, especially if they lack the support of a partner.

In the case of a drug-using woman, family relationships have often suffered considerable breakdown. The partner is often either absent or suffering from the effects of drug abuse himself. Pregnancy can sometimes have the effect of a rallying round 'for the baby's sake'; however mistrust, acrimony and bitterness make the situation fragile. If there can be some intervention, such as a family support group or counselling, fragile relationships can sometimes be strengthened.

Housing and housekeeping

A large proportion of chronic drug users will find themselves in accommodation unsuitable for the raising of young children. Housing problems are compounded when the user has learnt few coping skills such as preparing meals, shopping or hygiene. Coping with a budget is a problem when one is used to having to finance an addiction to heroin or crack. If the user is making an effort to stay off street drugs, a move away from their known environment is often the only realistic way of sustaining this.

Again, the user may not have the skills or the stamina to take their case to the relevant agencies and push for help. Housing agency staff are often mistrustful if they are aware of a drugs problem, and there is a feeling amongst users that they could be discriminated against if they disclose their status. If this situation is not addressed the user may attempt to make the best of unsuitable conditions and consequently set themselves up to fail. A common understanding of drug-related issues is needed by housing agencies and sensitivity is required to help advocate and support the user to establish herself.

Treatment and health: service provision issues

Ongoing involvement with a drugs agency can be a crucial factor if the mother is to cope successfully with a pregnancy and the new child. Methadone treatment can be a way of stabilizing someone's heroin addiction. By providing a substitute it affords the opportunity to obtain a free, clean supply of drugs and to move further away from the learnt lifestyle involved with the blackmarket merry-go-round. Once the user has stabilized their drug intake there is the opportunity to make a decision regarding moderation of intake or even complete detoxification under medical supervision. Many pregnant drug users have used the extra motivation of an expectant child to make a serious and sustained effort to beat their addiction, and some do succeed.

There are other health complications and risks associated with drug misuse that some users will be prone to. Hepatitis is spreading amongst drug users and can be transmitted far more easily than the more publicized HIV virus. Vaccination or preventative measures can be readily undertaken when the user is in contact with health agencies. Persistent poor injecting practice can have a debilitating effect on the body and can make it prone to serious infections such as septicaemia. Many users are seriously undernourished by an inadequate diet lacking in vitamins and vital minerals.

A large proportion of women addicted to heroin will experience a cessation of menstruation. Some believe that because of this they cannot get pregnant. This can lead the user to forgo contraception and to be unaware of the early signs of pregnancy. For these reasons, as well as the fear of authority, being judged as a bad person, or avoidance of facing up to a difficult reality, many women present to pre-natal or maternity services late into confinement.

It is difficult to offer someone support when they cannot hear you. The first priority when working with drug users is to reach them and inform them that help is at hand. So services within communities and outreach work are vital.

As mentioned above, the time factor is important when working with pregnant drug users. A system of priority status can ensure that valuable time is not wasted and needs can be assessed almost immediately.

Harm reduction is a key phrase in today's service provision. Abstinence is not always a realistic option for users; we must continue to work with those that choose to continue taking drugs. Access to clean injecting equipment and advice on safer injecting can improve the general health of users and reduce the spread of transmittable disease. Free contraception and family planning services can reduce the risk of unwanted pregnancies and sexually transmitted disease.

Merseyside Drugs Council – Liverpool Counselling Service

This agency has a long history of offering counselling to those whose lives are affected by drugs. These can be illegal drug users or prescribed drug users, as well as their parents and families.

The Liverpool Counselling Service offers ongoing support and counselling as well as a referral service to those in need of help from other agencies. Clients usually present in one of two ways; via the drop-in service where they can see the duty counsellor, or by referral from other agencies such as GPs, the probation service or prison.

The agency employs qualified counsellors who have experience of working with drug users. In addition to this, one counsellor specializes in working with the families of drug users and supports them one-to-one or in support groups. Access to prescribing is made through the GP Liaison Scheme, where users can be helped to find a GP, and their progress is monitored through the counselling service. This can be a boon to doctors who, often overstretched themselves, have traditionally found drug users a difficult group to work with effectively.

The agency has established links with local prisons and has found there is a great demand in prisons for effective harm reduction education and the provision of a pathway into services for those who need it when they return to the community.

In addition, those motivated to completely change their lifestyle and totally abstain from drugs may wish to enter a residential rehabilitation programme. This involves assessing clients' suitability for these programmes on behalf of social services, who will provide funds for them to enter one if necessary.

When working with vulnerable clients, who may be disclosing material they have never shared before, issues such as confidentiality and boundaries need to be clearly understood by all parties. As well as the expected qualities of the counsellor such as empathy and sensitivity, a framework for helping can be used. This allows the client to understand and review change in a step-by-step approach. It is not simply a case of listening, it is a challenging approach that recognizes the client's ability to understand their own feelings and tackle important issues, and their readiness to do so.

This framework is probably best illustrated by use of a real case history. No case is ever truly typical; this story however is presented in a form that hopefully demonstrates some of the rationale behind this type of approach. The name and some details have been changed to protect the anonymity of the client.

Anita

In common with many more heroin users today, Anita had had some contact with drugs services. When she progressed on to injecting the drug she had been introduced to the syringe exchange service where she had been accepted without question or fuss. She had suffered some bruising to her arm and a nurse at the syringe exchange had noticed this and offered some advice on safer injecting.

Anita felt accepted not just as a user but as a person in her own right. By not being pressed into others' values and/or persuasions to 'do something' about her drug use, Anita felt comfortable coming into these agencies. She felt they accepted her drug use as part of her choices and were not shocked by it. Hopefully, any concern they expressed would be for her as a person, not out of negative judgement of her practices.

The crisis stage

When Anita discovered she was pregnant she was horrified and immediately in distress. She had no plans to start a family and her partner had recently been sent to prison for drug-related offences. She was currently living with two other women users, one of whom was a sex worker.

She asked to speak to a counsellor and, in recognition of her crisis situation, she was seen immediately. She had a whole series of dilemmas that appeared to be insoluble and these presented themselves in the initial session as a torrent of questions to herself:

- Did she want a baby?
- Could she cope?
- Should she have this baby or should she consider an abortion?
- Should she stop using heroin – was it damaging the fetus?
- How would the father/family react?

Each issue raised feelings of guilt and despair and with it a craving to use yet more heroin in an attempt to block these feelings.

Most counselling relationships begin in crisis; it is a recognizable stage during which people think, feel and consequently act differently than normal. Everyday routines can become stressful and difficult, and the prospect of change is frightening. It is important that the counsellor recognizes this stage and does not attempt to give advice. Decisions made at this time can be seriously regretted later. Careful listening, warmth and empathy are all that is needed before the dilemmas can begin to be considered, and the process of planning begun.

The exploration stage

As the next couple of sessions progressed Anita began to accept her situation and was better prepared to look rationally at her dilemmas. She had yet to make any decision but was readily exploring options. She talked through the different scenarios and tried to imagine how she may feel about them. She looked at her support network and how she could add to this to help her cope. We discussed the option surrounding detoxification and how, when, and if this was likely to be achieved. This involved Anita taking a truly honest review of her drug use which proved to be a breakthrough in itself. We discussed the pros and cons of being prescribed the heroin substitute methadone, and its likely effects on both her and the unborn child. She began to talk about her relationship and fears for their future together.

As the crisis subsides, if the client feels comfortable with the counsellor, she is likely to want to explore all aspects of the problem, sometimes over and over again. It is extremely important that the counsellor is thoroughly knowledgeable and up-to-date on the issues surrounding drug use and pregnancy, but does not give advice, impose values or be judgmental. The client should feel that she arrived at her own decisions, for she alone will have to live with them.

The result of this could then be that the client later acknowledges she has taken control of her own life and has not been dependent on others. This can have a beneficial effect on self-esteem and confidence.

Decision-making and action

Shortly after this stage, Anita made the decision that she wanted to have the baby. Part of the reason was that she felt she needed to tackle her drug use and the baby would give her life some direction and purpose. She still felt very unsure about her relationship with the father but decided to inform him anyway. She was still routinely using heroin and did not want to risk miscarriage by the added strain of immediate detoxification. In view of this she decided to opt for a methadone course, aiming to reduce the dosage through the later terms of pregnancy. At this point a referral was made to the Drug Dependency Clinic where she would be seen as a priority and, from there, access to the community midwife with special responsibility for drug users would be established.

Once decisions are made the situation tends to become more real and we can begin to learn to cope with it. We can then prepare to take any actions that are required. This is often the time when we feel better and more energized. Using a drug such as heroin can provide an escape from thinking and feeling about problems and dilemmas and therefore decisions, though readily made by users, will often fail because they are unrealistic. The counselling sessions enabled Anita to examine her thoughts and feelings in open forum and as trust developed she was challenged more often and found it hard to avoid the issues.

Postscript

Life for Anita following her involvement with this agency was hardly straightforward. She managed to come off and stay off drugs during her pregnancy. She had a healthy baby boy and established a comfortable home with support from her family. When her partner returned from prison he moved in with her and they both relapsed. However, before their situation got completely out of control they contacted the agency and went back onto methadone treatment. They still use heroin occasionally but in general lead a stable life with plenty of love and care for the child. Anita would like to be completely drug free but recognizes her partner is weaker than she is, and when he uses she gives in. Despite this they have a generally happy relationship and would like another child.

We are aware that the drug users we have experience of are usually getting some sort of help and treatment and therefore may not be wholly representative of those presenting to maternity services. It is difficult not to be judgmental if you discover a woman in the early stages of labour wanting to go to the toilet for a 'hit' of heroin. Or when a social worker tells you of a client who arrives at a case conference, called about her children, stoned and falling asleep.

Both these situations have happened with clients of ours and it is these stories that stick in the mind and are passed around. We were flabbergasted on hearing them, as both clients had been very stable for a considerable time. It is only by understanding the user's perception of authority and their fear of being judged and controlled that we could understand why a heroin addict craves and uses their drug in these situations to excess.

By making an extra effort to show compassion and empathy to drug users we can be rewarded with profitable relationships that achieve genuine change. Non-judgmentality in care is the key to achieving this.

Conclusion

Although this book has tried to cover many issues, there are steps that need to be taken to move towards a better service for those vulnerable women and their children.

Education in schools, using project workers, is essential if children are to grow up aware of the problems surrounding drug use. Parents should be educated too.

Accessible and sympathetic support services, both statutory and voluntary, should educate and support in the areas of drugs, contraception and prostitution, as well as health, housing and benefits.

Education and support for student midwives, midwives, midwife teachers, medical staff and social workers must be ongoing. Attitudes are always difficult to change but it helps if people can recognise that they may have an attitude!

There needs to be sharing of research and experience within a combined forum for all professionals acknowledging expertise, experience and commitment to care.

Catherine Siney

Appendix

DRUG WITHDRAWAL ASSESSMENT CHART

Name:_____   Unit number: _____
DOB: _____   Time of birth:_____

Minor signs e.g. jitters, sweating, yawning do not require treatment.

Consider treatment if any of the following signs are present:

- Profuse vomiting

- Profuse watery diarrhoea

- Tube feeds required due to incoordinate sucking

- Unsettled after two consecutive feeds

Has the baby settled at all since its last feed?
Please place a tick in the YES or NO box.

Date:						
Time:	04.00	08.00	12.00	16.00	20.00	24.00
YES:						
NO:						

Date:						
Time:	04.00	08.00	12.00	16.00	20.00	24.00
YES:						
NO:						

Date:						
Time:	04.00	08.00	12.00	16.00	20.00	24.00
YES:						
NO:						

GUIDELINES FOR MANAGEMENT OF DRUG WITHDRAWAL

- Minor signs do not require treatment
- Withdrawal from opiates may occur <24 hours (e.g. heroin)
- Withdrawal from opioids may occur 3-4 days after birth
  (e.g. methadone)
- Polydrug use may delay or skew withdrawal signs
- Aim of treatment is comfort not sedation
- Baby is reviewed daily by paediatric staff.

Treatment plan

Level 4
0.04 mgs/kg morphine sulphate   oral preparation given 4 hourly

Level 3
0.03 mgs/kg morphine sulphate   oral preparation given 4 hourly

Level 2
0.02 mgs/kg morphine sulphate   oral preparation given 4 hourly

Level 1
0.01 mgs/kg morphine sulphate   oral preparation given 4 hourly

Level reduced every 24 hours if the baby is feeding well and settling better between feeds.

If the feeding and settling does not improve or profuse watery stools and profuse vomiting continue – discuss with senior paediatrician.

Other medication may be required, e.g. diazepam for benzodiazepine use or chloral hydrate for cocaine/crack use.

If pharmaceutical treatment is not required, the mother will still require support to help her comfort the baby. Cuddling and swaddling is helpful. An infant soother ('dummy') may be necessary.

Index

G

Genital herpes 126
Genital warts 130
Gestational hypertension 58
Gonorrhoea 120
Group B streptococcus (GBS) 125
Growth retardation 70, 72
GUM clinics 135

H

HAART 95
Hepatitis B 14, 32, 82
  diagnosis 84
  immunisation 87
  mother to baby transmission 83
  screening 87
  vaccine 87
Hepatitis C 89
Hepatitis D 89
Heroin 5, 57, 64, 146
  addicts 3
Herpes simplex virus (HSV) 126
HIV 94, 139
  Antenatal testing 96
  mother to baby transmission 102
  prevalence 15
  testing 15, 94
Human papilloma virus (HPV) 130
Hyperemesis 57

I

Inebriates Act 1888 2
Infant Life
  (Preservation) Act (1929) 15
Injection, techniques 28, 52
In-patient detoxification 41
Institute for the Study of
  Drug Dependence (ISDD) 19
Intra-uterine contraceptive
  device (IUD) 109
Intrauterine deaths 58
Intrauterine growth
  retardation (IUGR) 61

L

Labour 30
Late booking 26
LGDF 10
Liverpool Drug Dependency
  Unit (LDDU) 29
Liverpool Model 26
Low birth weight 70, 72
Lunacy Act (1890) 2

M

Marijuana 62
Maternal deaths 60
Maternal rights 15
Mental Deficiency Act (1913) 2
Methadone 4, 25, 29, 45, 57, 64, 70
  oral 40
Misuse of Drugs Act (1971) 4
Morphine sulphate 76
Morphine 57, 75
Multiple pregnancies 58

N

Naloxone hydrochloride 31
Naloxone 45
Needle and Syringe
  Exchanges (NSE) 52
Neonatal Abstinence
  Syndrome (NAS) 59, 62, 70, 73
NNRTIs 98
NRTIs 98
Nutrition 57

O

Opiate withdrawal 45
Opiates 7, 57, 70, 109
Opium 2
Osteomyelitis 50
Overdosage 44

P

Palatal clefting 70
Paragoric 75
Parent education 27
Pharmacy Act (1868) 2
Placental abruption 60, 72
Poisons and Pharmacy Act (1908) 2
Post-delivery care 31
Pre-conception care 26, 112
Prematurity 70, 72
Preterm deliveries 58
Prison 37, 157
Prostitution 37, 56, 108, 138
Pseudomonas aeruginosa 50
Pubic lice 134
Pulmonary vascular
  granulomatosis 46

R

Rehabilitation 42, 157
Respiratory distress syndrome 70
Respiratory system 46
Rolleston Committee 3

S

Safe sex 135
Scabies 134
SCODA 10
Screening 14, 63
Septicaemia 50
Sexually transmitted
  infections (STIs) 116
Skin infections 47
Skin necrosis 49
Small-for-gestational-age 58, 60, 62
Spermicides 110
Staphylococcus aureus 49, 50
Stillbirth 72
Sudden Infant Death
  Syndrome 59, 72
Syphilis 117

T

Temazepam 51, 61, 146
Tetanus 50
Thrombosis 57, 60
Tobacco 7, 65, 73
Training, staff 33
Treatment agencies 38
Trichomoniasis 132
Tubercular disease 47

U

Ultrasound scan 27
Uterine blood flow 60

V

Vaginal candidosis 133
Venepuncture 49
Venous access 65
Voice 51

W

Withdrawal 24
  in pregnancy 45
  neonatal 12, 61

Z

Zidovudine 103